Y0-CAT-177

You Better Not Cry

The Lemonade Collection™

Janet Barré

The Collector's Edition
Statement of Authenticity
1 of 100
Printed June 22, 2001

Collector's Edition prizes will be awarded through:

HuckleberryPress.com

You Better Not Cry

A Huckleberry Press Book
The Lemonade Collection™

Text Copyright © 2001 by Janet Barré
Photographs Copyright © by Janet Barré
All other Copyrights © 2001 by Huckleberry Press

All rights reserved. No part of this book may be reproduced or utilized in any
form by photostat, microfilm, xerography, electronic, or any other means, or
incorporated into any information retrieval system, electronic or mechanical,
without the written permission of the publisher.

All inquiries should be addressed to:
Huckleberry Press.com
P.O. Box 573
So. Glastonbury, CT 06073-0573
1-800-606-0541

Edited by Noreen Wise

Reading guides can be found at:
HuckleberryPress.com

Made in the United States
Publication Year 2001
10 9 8 7 6 5 4 3
ISBN 1-58584-555-8 • LCCN: 2001 131078

Cover and graphic design by The Huckleberry Press creative team:
Liz Wethington, Paul Horton, Noreen Wise,
Christopher Alix, Jill Benford

Three percent of the net revenues of all Huckleberry Press products
will be donated to the Magic Foundation.™

For My Daughter, Tabitha...
Without her encouragement, these written words
would have remained imprisoned in the
dictionary of my mind.
Sometimes with annoyance, sometimes with grace,
she accepted the responsibility, real or imagined,
for being the wind beneath my wings.
Look, Tabitha, I'm soaring!
Fly with me!!!

Acknowledgments

Robin, Mark and Tabitha, you have become my teachers. It is my honor to be your Mom. Thank you. I love you all... five. Because of your strength of character you have blossomed as unique, extraordinary and beautiful friends of mine. Each one of you is proof that there is a Creator and that He, indeed, is love.

To Craig, I know you're there; I'm here.

Thank you, Jackie Therrian, for taking on the daunting task of deciphering my handwriting. Thank you, Kim Charles, for nagging me to find a publisher. Thank you, David Picone, for helping me to fill out my forms and mail out my manuscripts. Thank you, Dave, for copying and sorting my hundreds and hundreds of pages.

To everyone who was aware that I was in need and reached out to try to transform my circumstances, THANK YOU. You are etched in my heart, for you are the ones who inch-by-inch became an integral part of my metamorphasis. I have memorized your faces and your expressions of kindness. To be esteemed by each of you is humbling. You know who you are; I know who you are; God knows who you are. You are the giants in my life.

Author's Note:

This is a true story. Although I chose to change most of the names of the participants, the events are just as they happened back in the 1930's and 1940's. Yes, with God's help I weathered the hurricane of 1938 and all the other storms that blew my way.

Ecclesiastes 3:1-8

For everything there is an appointed time,
and a time for every affair under the heavens:

A time for birth, and a time to die;
A time to plant, and a time to uproot what was planted.
A time to kill, and a time to heal;
A time to break down, and a time to build.
A time to weep, and a time to laugh;
A time to wail, and a time to skip about.
A time to throw stones away,
and a time to bring stones together;
A time to embrace,
and a time to keep away from embracing.
A time to seek, and a time to give up as lost;
A time to keep, and a time to throw away.
A time to rip apart, and a time to sew together,
A time keep quiet, and a time to speak.
A time to love, and a time to hate;
A time for war, and a time for peace.

1

A Time To Rip Apart

"Good morning, here's your beautiful brand new baby daughter, Claudette."

"Take her away."

"Take her away? It's time to feed her."

"Take her away."

"I can't take her away; it's time for you to nurse her."

"Give her a bottle and just TAKE HER AWAY!!!"

Oh no, "SHE" did it again. Mrs. Monroe is beating on the front door screaming, "I know he's in there." SHE's hiding him under the table covered with a cloth that goes to the floor, a white tablecloth—a white tablecloth with a beautiful pattern. A beautiful pattern hiding ugly Mr. Monroe. SHE screams back at Mrs. Monroe, "He's not here!"

Oh God, SHE's going to burn in hell for lying. I don't like her very much, but I don't want her to burn in hell. I'm terrified. The five of us, Margaret, Naomi, Jouny, Robert, and I, are terrified. There are seven of us in the room. SHE's angry as usual. Mr. Monroe, I hope, is dead under the table. I only hope that he's dead so that this will stop happening. Maybe he can come back to life in his own house. Maybe God will do that for me. God must want to make a little four-year-old girl happy. That's it! Talk to God, but for heaven's sake, you better not cry. SHE *hates* that. It will only make her more angry, and you don't want to make HER more angry.

Thank God the banging stops. Mrs. Monroe is gone. At least Mr. Monroe didn't have to die. He just sneaks out the back door saving God some extra work. The real trick now is to look and act as though nothing happened. When Daddy comes home from work, he's going to be very tired because he works, I think, for somebody called WPA. All the grown-ups keep talking about the depression and how bad it is. I don't think that we've had that yet.

I know we five young ones had the whooping cough and the measles and the mumps, but I never heard the doctor say any of us had the depression. Maybe it's just something grown-ups get. I think they said Margaret had Scarlet Fever. That's when you stay in a dark bedroom and everybody thinks you're going to die. Nanny stayed in one of the bedrooms. She was very short. If you're four years old and you think someone's short, she must be very short. After a while I didn't know how short she was, because I never saw her anymore. I knew that she was in the bedroom, and the doctor gave her shots. After a while she wasn't even in the bedroom. I kept looking for her, but she was gone. No one ever said where she went. Maybe she had the depression. All I know is that she wasn't anywhere to be found. That made me sad, but I knew that I'd better not cry. Then I thought that maybe somebody found her. That made me feel a little better.

I like my bed. It's a little white iron bed. I feel safe there. Oh dear, Daddy's home. I hate all of the yelling. He says to her, "I'm going to go in and check on Claudette." I keep my eyes closed and pretend to be asleep. I don't want to worry him by letting him know that I heard the yelling. He pulls the covers up over me and leaves the room, leaving the door slightly open. Then, horrors of horrors, I hear him lie!! He says to her, "She's asleep." I cry very, very quietly and beg God all night to please forgive him for lying. It was my fault. I made him think I was asleep. I don't want him to burn in Hell. Blame me. It wasn't his fault. I was very happy to find him alive in the morning. It was good to know that God was hearing this little girl's prayers. And please don't let Daddy get the depression like Nanny. He didn't.

In the morning the four of them go off to school. I'm not old enough yet. That makes me sad. I want to go to school. However, there is a surprise for me this morning, a lollipop with Tootsie Roll inside. Daddy said, "You can't eat it now, but you can have it later in the day." Could there possibly be a more wonderful father in the whole world? I think not. He has to leave now to see that Mr. WPA. I've always wished that I could meet him.

Mrs. Boreck, who lives upstairs, is banging on her floor with the broom. That means that SHE is supposed to go upstairs and visit. SHE leaves me at the table with my eggs and my toast and goes upstairs. I like that. I'd rather be by myself because I never know what to say to her.

Look at that. Even though it's raining outside, the sun is out right here on my plate—two suns. Eggs can be suns if you want them to be. I won't eat them right away because I want the sun to last a little longer. Oh, oh, here SHE comes. Make those suns disappear. "Yes, Ma'am, I'm finished."

Great! It's stopped raining. Now I can go ride my tricycle. Actually it's my brother's tricycle. Here come the garbage men. I always feel sorry for the garbage men. I don't know why, I just do. Maybe it's because they have to ride in that truck with everybody's garbage. Those big green flies make me sick just to look at them. The garbage men must really get sick having them fly around their heads all day. I wonder if they take the garbage home?

I ask one of them, "Do you have a little boy or girl?" When he answers, "Yes," I say, "Then give them this tricycle. They'd probably like it." He thanks me and takes it. He takes the tricycle!!! I can't believe it. I was being polite by offering it, and he was supposed to say "No thank you." That's what we were taught. When people offer you something, especially food, or you offer them something, they or you are supposed to say "No thank you, but thank you just the same."

It has something to do with everybody's being poor from having the depression. It makes you poor and not sick. So now, I had to try to figure out again what Nanny had that made her go away and never come back. If the depression just makes you poor, the doctor wouldn't have had to give her shots for that. If my life has so many unanswered questions at four years old, what will I do at five? Surely my brain will break. So many questions and no one to ask. Daddy is too tired, and SHE is too angry. My two sisters, seven and ten years older than me, don't seem interested; and my two brothers, two and four years older than I am, just like to torment me.

I remember Robert saying to me, "Put your hand on the flat iron. It won't burn you." SHE told me to never put my hand near the iron. However, I need somebody to play with me, so I'll have to make Robert happy. I do what he tells me to do. The burn is horrible. Of course, I get a beating for it. I can't tattle on Robert because he'll get angry and never play with me again.

"How about the razor blade?" Robert says, "Here, just run this razor blade across your finger. It won't hurt." His reason? "Daddy uses a razor blade on his face, and it doesn't hurt him! It won't hurt. Do it or I won't play with you."

There SHE was, furious because I had blood all over the place. Another whipping for being "stupid!" And, "You better not cry or you'll get more!"

"Yes, Ma'am." I can't tattle or I'll lose my "playmate."

Probably the most fun my two brothers have tormenting me is with the magazines. They show me pictures of people in a magazine and tell me that if I don't do what they tell me to do, I will end up in the magazine. "And you know what happens to the magazines. Daddy burns them with the garbage out in the backyard." I'm so scared my stomach hurts. I obey them. I'm four years old.

How do I explain the tricycle's being gone? I could lie

and say I left it and somebody took it. No! You don't want to have her catch you in a lie. And then there's God. First she'd beat me with the strap, and then God would burn me forever. Is life this hard for all little four-year-old girls? Well, I get the strap, but at least it's for telling the truth. And I didn't cry. Frankly, I think that the garbage man should have been beaten with the strap and then go to Hell with Mr. Monroe!

2

A Time To Move

Move? I'll never see Mrs. Hodge again? I don't want to believe that. She is so pretty and wears such beautiful clothes. I love to watch her hang the clothes on the clothesline. I'm glad that she has two little boys, because that gives her a lot of laundry to hang out on the line, and I can watch her longer. I feel so good when she calls me over and talks with me, because she's so kind. Sometimes she hugs me. I worry about her though because her stairs go up so high, like a mountain. I get afraid that she'll fall off. I get even more afraid when her husband comes home. How could anyone be so mean to someone so pretty and sweet? His whole family is very afraid of him. The grown-ups say he "drinks." I drink. Everybody I know drinks. SHE always tells us, "Drink your milk." Maybe that's why Robert and Jouny are mean to me, because they drink. I don't know though, they drink the same things I drink, and I don't feel mean. I just feel scared. So many questions...

I wonder if we're going to take my bed? I hope that nobody tells Mr. or Mrs. Monroe where we're moving. I'm very sure that Daddy won't tell them. I wish we could take the trees. They must be the most beautiful trees in the whole world. In the summer they're like a huge green tunnel. In the autumn they're, pretty? No. They're more than pretty, they're beautiful? No. They're more than beautiful. What's more than beautiful? Oh, I wish I knew more words. Maybe when I go to school I'll learn more ways to say things. It must be wonderful to be able to read. When I can read, the first book I'm going to read is the dictionary.

The house looks so empty. I hope Mrs. Boreck gets a new neighbor fast so that she'll be able to bang on the floor with the broom and have someone to chat with. Well, we don't have to pack up the tricycle, do we? Anyway, it's probably covered with green flies by now.

I'm glad Daddy doesn't smoke cigarettes. They smell terrible. Maybe the movers will forget to move HER cigarettes. I never see anyone else's mother smoke. It scares me. SHE always tells us not to light matches, but she puts that white thing in her mouth and sets it on fire. I'm so afraid that her hair will go up in smoke. I don't understand it. SHE's so afraid of lightning that we all have to go into a closet or get under the bed when there's a storm. I think I'd be more afraid of setting myself on fire by lighting a match to something in my mouth! I'll never do that!! The truck is here; I better not cry.

The number of our house is $43^{1/2}$. Nobody else that I know of has a half on their number. A porch, I really like porches. I especially like the porch in the summer when it rains. You just turn the two green wicker rocking chairs upside down, cover them with a blanket, and you can travel anywhere you want to in your head.

The rocking chairs are especially wonderful when it's very, very dark. You close your eyes while you're rocking and pretend you're way up in the sky. Then, you open your eyes quickly, and there are the stars flashing so close to you that you know that you can just reach out and touch them. Of course, I know that they're lightening bugs; however, eggs can be suns, so lightening bugs can be stars. Hmmm... I love to think.

I guess it's $43^{1/2}$ because it's set in back between two other houses. Each of the houses has three floors. There are two families in one house and three in the other. There is a stone wall that runs across the front of these two houses. In between the houses is a narrow sidewalk going to the back where our house is. There are three rooms on the first floor—the kitchen, dining room and living room. They're not very large rooms. The walls are a yellowish painted plaster. There is a full-length cabinet in the dining room with a door. Behind the door are the most beautiful dishes I have ever seen. The purples, the greens, they're so, pretty? So happy? Oh please, words, words, I need more words.

Here they come with Daddy's big roll top desk. There's no place to put it except in the dining room. I'm glad, because now it's in a spot where I can see it every day. If I say, "Please," Daddy opens his desk and lets me look at all those wonderful drawers and cubbyholes filled to the brim with things. "I'm sure that if this desk could be mine, I would be the happiest four-year-old going on five in the whole world. In one of the little drawers is a lock of my baby hair and a little gold baby ring. The hair is a blond ringlet, so blonde that it's almost white. The ring is a plain gold band. I can only look at them, but they are not to be touched. They are so beautiful that I shiver inside whenever I can get Daddy to take them out and let me look at them. There is just one thing about this desk that seems to make HER unhappy. There is one locked drawer, and Daddy always has the key. I don't think that that's important; however, that thinking will change.

There is a flight of stairs, ten to be exact, going from the kitchen to the upstairs where there are three bedrooms, one bathroom, and one closet. At this time there are seven people, two parents and five children, which unbeknownst to me, would quickly increase by another five children, all boys.

The attic is scary and big. *I* think it's big. It will be a wonderful place to go to when it's raining. There is a hallway off to the left of the bottom of the staircase that leads to a pantry. Also off of that hallway is the cellar door. I can't wait to get our first load of coal. I love the noise it makes as it comes down the chute. There's a great big tree stump on a dirt floor. Daddy says it's for splitting the wood. I hate to look at that ax!

Outside there are bushes separating our yard from Mr. Caferty on one side and Mr. Hobart on the other. Mr. Caferty hates children. How did my legs get all cut and bloody? From the barbed wire that Mr. Caferty strung all through his bushes. I think he could have just asked us not to go through his bushes.

Do I just think there's somebody up on that top floor of Mr. Caferty's house peeking out the window at us? There really is somebody there. This is scary.

The house on the left has three families in it. Mr. and Mrs. Becker live on the third floor. She's strange. "They" say that she was holding a spoon during an electrical storm and was hit by lightning. On the second floor are a mom and dad and several sons.

On the bottom floor is some kind of a minister. The other kids are so mean to his son. They tell him to go in and ask his father for the keys to the rectum. They say he thinks that means the rectory. I don't know what the rectory or the rectum is, but I wish he'd stop asking his father, because every time the kids send him to say it, his father hits him. I guess I understand him. He wants the kids to like him and to play with him. He's different though from me. He cries. I know better. "Yes, Ma'am"... "No, Ma'am."

3

A Time To Explore

Well, now I own a new word: move. I thought it just meant "Get out of the way." This is exciting. One word can mean two things. *Move over... Just move away from me! ...Oh, yes, we moved here in the summer... We used to live on that street, but then we had to move to this street...*

This is fun. I wonder what the priest did to Mrs. Murphy. She told Mrs. Conroy that when she went to church, Monsignor O'Brien really moved her. I wonder if he told her to get out of the way, or if he drove the furniture truck to her house when she moved in up the street? Monsignor O'Brien always used to say, "When you send your children to church, give them more than a pinny. When you send them to the movies, you give them more than a pinny. So give them more than a pinny for the basket." I know Daddy paid the moving men. I wonder if Mrs. Murphy paid Monsignor O'Brien to move her?

Mrs. Murphy has a beautiful, clean, white house with a great big front porch. I think they're the rich people. She looks rich. Everyday she walks by to go to the grocery store at the bottom of the hill. She looks round and clean.
"Hello, Mrs. Murphy."
"Hello, Claudette."

We have a mulberry tree in our yard, and we also have two pear trees. Everyone should have a mulberry tree so that they can watch those little worms spin their silky webs. Besides, I don't think that there's a better climbing tree than our mulberry. When you get up there high enough, you can see half of the world I'm sure. And the pear trees aren't just for pears. A pear tree can help you to look like a beautiful princess. Well, the blossoms can anyway. Just put one of those lacy white blossoms with the pretty green leaves over each ear and fasten them with a bobby pin. If people didn't already know that I was just Claudette, they probably would have believed that I was a real princess. I'm sure they would!

We have new linoleum on the downstairs floors. What a delicious smell! I especially like our kitchen table. It has a drawer and a top that you can write on. I think it's called porcelain. Somebody is always leaving a message in pencil for somebody else, and then you can just wash it off with water and Old Dutch cleanser. We used to have an icebox, and now we have a refrigerator.

The top of the refrigerator is a shelf for everything. "Just put it on the top of the refrigerator." How high is that pile going to get? Only SHE and Daddy have a closet. It's in their bedroom. There's a little storage room under the attic stairs. Not much "hanging space" for all these people. I guess that's what the doors and doorknobs are for. At least in our house they are.

There is a cot with an army blanket on it in the living room. There are also two chairs, a radio, and tables with lamps on them. We used to have a rug that you could play Tiddley Winks on. You could snap them very easily. I love to play pick-up sticks, too. I'm pretty good at that. There's another game that I'm good at. Whenever Dr. Strictor and his wife, Claudette, (I was named after her) come to visit us, he throws a penny and a dime on the floor, and everybody yells, "Go for the big one, Claudette. Go for the big one." When I pick up the penny, they always laugh and laugh. I guess this game makes them really happy.

When I feel very, very brave, I go down in the cellar. I love the way it smells, damp and earthy. I know it's a dirt floor, but I like to say it's earth. Dirt sounds like something bad. The sound of the word "earth" makes my ears happy.

The opening between the dining room and the living

23

room has sort of a round top. I heard someone say it is arched, so I guess that's what you call it, an arch. There is a picture on the wall that is made of all little seashells. It's a picture of a beautiful garden with hollyhocks. My insides get all funny when I look at it. I'm going to have a garden that looks like that someday. As a matter of fact, we have pink hollyhocks growing up against the house that reach right up to the second-floor bedroom windows. They are so lovely. I have a new word.

There is a metal roof over the porch. You can get onto it by climbing out of the bathroom window. If you're very quiet, no one will know that you're there. You can also climb over the side, shimmy down the post, land on the railing, and then get onto the ground. It would be the perfect way to get away in the middle of the night if you wanted to run away from home. Hmmm...

If you are very brave—which I'm not—you can look out the hall window into our neighbor's backyard and watch him chop chickens' heads off and then watch the chickens run around without heads, with blood spurting out. Some people think this is funny. *Funny*, (Fun-E). *adj.* 1. Causing amusement or laughter. 2. Humorous. 3. Laughable... It isn't funny!

Mr. Sanders is funny. He owns the candy store on the corner. It's really a printing shop, but he also sells penny candy and ice cream. I love the sound of the press and the smell of the ink. I especially love the candy. I don't really like the kind called "Squirrel Nuts," but I get five for a penny. They are kind of like caramel with little chunks of nuts in them. I can just suck all of the caramel off and spit the nuts out. It's really the best buy in the store; nothing else is five for a penny. It takes me a very long time to make a decision. There are so many choices. There are really so many other candies that taste better—but five for a penny? "I'll have the Squirrel Nuts, please."... "Thank you, Mr. Sanders."

Mr. Sanders' wife makes me think of Blondie Bumstead. She has blond hair, too. They live in a little house right next door to their store. Sometimes she lets me come in and talk with her; I like that. They have a son named "Gene," or maybe it's "Eugene." Mr. Sanders said that Gene is to go to college someday. I wonder where college is? Sometimes we go to Fall River to visit Grampa and Gramma.

Up the block on the next corner is where they sell the cigarettes. SHE puts the money in the corner of a handkerchief and ties a knot. "Tell the man you want a package of Pall Malls."

Oh no, my hair is going to smell like Pall Malls. SHE's going to spit on her fingers to wet my hair and then roll it up in rags to make it curly. It scares me half to death when she does it with the cigarette hanging out of her mouth. If those ashes fall on me, I'll scream! Wait, I better not cry.

On the way back from the Pall Mall store is an empty lot. Well, it's not completely empty. It just doesn't have a house there. It's filled with bushes, trees, and flowers. Of course, the most wonderful flowers of all are the purple violets. God must have said, "What is the most beautiful flower that I can make?" And then He answered Himself and said, "Purple Violets." I'm sure that He really likes the white violets that He made, but I know the purple ones are His favorite.

There is another little girl across the street. The grown-ups say that her father is a bookie. Hmmm... "Bookie." Well, he owns a little store where you can buy cigarettes, cigars, magazines, and books. I guess that's it; he sells a lot of books. Their house is so clean that I want to go in there all the time. My friend gets to take a bath every night. That must be heaven. Her mom puts her in the bathtub with bubble bath and bathes her and dries her off and puts her in her pajamas. It's not like that in our house.

In the summer my friend and I lie down in the grass in her yard and try to see shapes of animals and other things in the clouds. Sometimes we take turns rubbing each other's arms, making the hair stand up straight. It looks funny. One day I went home and hold HER that we did this funny thing. SHE said, "That's disgusting. That's a form of masturbation!" Two more words I'll have to look up when I can read—disgusting and masturbation. (When I was about ten years old and able to read well, I looked up "masturbation.")

Masturbation (Mas'-ter-ba-shen) *noun,* The act of exciting the genitals to orgasm, by means, as manual contact, other than sexual intercourse. All these words to describe rubbing my arm to make the hair stand up? I don't get it; I thought that being able to look in the dictionary would answer all my questions. It just gives me more questions!

Directly across the street is where Ronald lives. He is so nice. His mother and daddy are so nice, too. We would become really good friends over the years even though I would find out that he was a Nazi. I don't really know what a Nazi is, except that it has to do with being German. Bobby's mother and daddy are German. So he has to be German. There is a war going on—whatever a war is—and all the Germans are Nazis. A lot of the kids are being nasty and mean to Ronald. I feel very sorry for him because I know it makes him sad. If Ronald and his mother and father are Nazis, then Nazis must be very nice people.

4

A Time To Learn

THIS IS IT! Finally, finally, finally, I'm going to school.

"Naomi is in Tenth Grade. Margaret is in Seventh Grade. Jouny (we call him this because he is a Junior) is in Fourth Grade. Robert is in Second Grade. And Claudette is in Kindergarten. Yes, they're all in school now. No, there are no other children at home."

When I hear her tell people this, it's like having songs in my ears. I love to sing. I sing a lot. I heard someone say that daddy liked to sing. SHE has a very nice singing voice, too. All my brothers and sisters like to sing. I wonder if I'll sing in school?

I can't believe how scared I am. I know that this is what I want to do. So why am I so afraid? "Miss Hennessee," that's a funny name. I wonder if we'll read a book today. I want to read so badly. On Sunday I put the funny papers on the floor, and then I put my elbows down and rest my chin on my hands. I let my eyes go back and forth very slowly so that everybody will think I know how to read. I'm sure I fool everybody.

Go get our mats? What are those for? We have to take a nap? On the floor? I want to read a book. Oh no, the water is starting to fall out of my eyes. I'm not crying. Please, God, don't let me cry.

"Miss Hennessee, Claudette's crying."

Why doesn't he mind his own business? She's going to hate me. Here she comes. Bury your head. I feel her hand on me. She's going to hit me. I can't believe it. She's putting me on her lap, and she's rocking me.

"Everything will be all right, Claudette; everything will be all right."

She smells so good. I wonder if I can stay here forever. I love you, Miss Hennessee.

This little building where I am in kindergarten is called the little homestead. It's a very, very old building. The big school is further back. Mr. Drake, who is our janitor (my new word), lives in this building. Every Memorial Day he dresses up in his old army uniform and speaks to all the children about our country. We all sing songs about the flag, and we recite (another new word) poems. "Recite" means that we say the poem over and over so many times that finally we can say it out loud without looking at the paper. We can recite it because we "memorized" it. I am so proud of my words that I think I'll burst.

It's getting very, very dark outside. The sky looks scary. Why is it getting so windy? Look at that rain coming down. Something is very wrong. Everybody is starting to cry. I won't cry. Why is Miss Hennessee telling us to get ready to go home? We haven't been here that long.

Everyone is saying there's a hurricane. What's that? Why are Naomi and Margaret and Jouny and Robert here in a taxicab? I'd better get in fast. I'm so scared; this is the most scared I've ever been. We're all going to die! Every street we try to go up has trees falling over in the road. I don't believe we made it. Run! Run as fast as you can into the house. The house looks spooky with just candles for lights. I don't want to go to bed! Please don't make me!

Maybe if I just pull myself up into a tight little ball and keep my head under the pillow and the covers, nothing will hurt me. That wind is so loud. I know it's going to break this whole house into little pieces. Please, please stop the rain. It's going to smash the window. "Somebody, hold me," I'm screaming in my head. "Somebody, hold me." I better not cry.

I can't believe we didn't all die last night. The sunshine

is beautiful. Let me take a peek out the window. Oh no, the yard is all broken. Everything is broken. No! No! No! My mulberry tree is broken. Everyone's trees are broken. My heart is broken. Please don't let my school be broken.

It's still here. Now I can breathe better. If my school was broken, I don't think that I would want to breathe any more. The big school in back of mine is all right, too. It's a very big, white, wooden building. My two brothers are already there. I wonder how it feels to be in the big school?

"My name is Miss Chagerty, and I am your first grade teacher."

I think she's very, very old. Her printing is very neat. I want to print like that. I can print my name. That must be so much fun to print on the blackboard with the chalk. Look at that—M I S S C H A G E R T Y.

The kids told me that she's "Miss" Chagerty and not "Mrs." Chagerty because she's not married. Lady teachers can't get married. If they do, then they lose their jobs. Men teachers can get married, but not lady teachers. I guess we'll have to be their children.

We're going to learn the alphabet. I can already sing it. I'll be happier when I can print it. These pencils are kind of fat. I love the way this paper smells. Aa Bb Cc Dd Ee Ff, I want my letters to look just like Miss Chagerty's. I think I'm getting pretty good at this.

I'm glad it's time to sing. This is one of my favorites: *Let the ball roll. Let the ball roll, no matter where it may go. Let the ball roll. Let the ball roll. It has to stop sometime, you know.* This is one of our "Safety First" songs. Miss Chagerty asks me to sing all by myself sometimes. She says I have a very nice voice. "Thank you, Miss Chagerty." I love school, and I love Miss Chagerty. Books! We're getting books!

Why can't I stay in this class with Miss Chagerty for second grade? I heard some of the teachers say that the second grade class is too big, so they need to have two second grades. Some who were in Miss Chagerty's class for first grade would stay with her for second grade. Please, please let me stay!

I don't like my new teacher at all. I'm sure she doesn't like me either. All the teachers look like cozy mothers. She just yells and gets nervous and wears bright red lipstick and nail polish. Please stop yelling; I can hear you. SHE's not going to stop. I hate yelling. I guess I'll just think about something else.

I wonder who he is? SHE said he's Uncle Jack. I didn't know I had an Uncle Jack. I know I have a Gramma, an Aunt Celia, and an Uncle Herman. I don't have a Grampa any more. I felt so sad when I saw him in his bed because he looked so sick. I heard them say he had "water on the knee." Grampa is a doctor, so I don't know why he can't fix himself. It was so much fun to visit them in Fall River.

Their house was the loveliest place I had ever seen. I remember that I was sitting at a large dining room table with all of my brothers and sisters, my parents, and Gramma and Grampa. The dishes were too beautiful to put food on. As we would finish each course, Laura, the maid, would appear like magic. We discovered Gramma's secret. She had a little buzzer under the table that she would push with her foot. It would sound out in the kitchen, and Laura would know that it was time to come in. I wouldn't be unhappy if I could live in that house. After Grampa died, Gramma never wanted to see us or speak to us again. I can't imagine why. Why wouldn't she want to see her own son?

I never saw her again that I can recall; but I remember her, and I remember Aunt Celia and Uncle Herman. But I don't remember any Uncle Jack. I wonder where he came from? I don't know why, but I don't like him. His nose looks like it has red berries all over it, and he has false teeth that click. I hate the way he smells. He smells like cigarettes all the time and whiskey. I hope he never comes back. He should stay in his own house.

"Claudette, I'm talking to you. Go up to the blackboard and write the name 'Christopher Columbus' underneath where I just wrote it."

"Yes, Ma'am." Hmmm... I think I'm a very good printer.

I think I'm a great printer. I think I am such an excellent printer that they should let me skip this grade and get away from this woman. Somebody should get her some nail polish remover.

5

A Time For God

Why does SHE look like that? I hate the way she comes in the house and takes her dress off, just sitting around in her slip, especially now that she keeps getting fatter and fatter.

Why is *he* here all the time? Why is SHE ironing all of his shirts? SHE won't even iron a handkerchief for daddy. I smooth out every little tiny corner. He said that I do a great job.

Kiss Uncle Jack good night? I'll do it, but I'll hate it. He stinks! I can't believe that I have to do this. Why is he always sitting here listening to the baseball game on our radio on the weekends? If he weren't here, I could listen to the opera. I love to hear the voice of the man who explains it. I wish I could meet him. People think I'm crazy because I love the opera. They say, "How can you listen to all that screaming?" I'm going to sing in the opera someday. I'm going to be on the stage in a beautiful gown and sing my heart out. Thank you, God, for making music and singing.

He makes me nervous when he's here, and SHE is out at the Bingo. SHE goes to Bingo fourteen times a week. SHE goes every afternoon and every night. Her dresses don't fit her any more.

SHE's going to have a what? A baby? That's what's in her stomach? How is it going to get out? When is it going to come out? Where are we going to put it? Eight people in the house?

"Your mother had a little boy."

I wish she had had a little girl. I already have two brothers. SHE keeps the crib in her room with daddy.

Now I know what a priest looks like. He came to our house and said that God sends a loaf of bread with every baby. That wouldn't last this family for one meal! God is going to have to do better than that. Who is God? I recite my prayer every night. *Now I lay me down to sleep. I pray the Lord my sole to keep. If I should die before I wake, I pray the Lord my sole to take.* What would God want with my shoes?

Now, I'm learning to memorize and recite the LORD'S PRAYER. I asked HER, "What is God's name, because it says 'hallowed be thy name'?" SHE said, "It's God."

That doesn't make sense. My father's name is Allan. How can God's name be God? I said it over to myself. *Our Father, who art in Heaven. Hallowed be thy name.* His name must be "Hallowed." SHE just doesn't know it. I'm not going to argue with her. *Thy kingdom come, thy will be done...* What is the kingdom?

"Go to sleep."

"Yes, Ma'am, good night."

I wonder why we don't go to church? I learned my prayers, and I learned that God burns people in Hell if they're bad. I don't know where Hell is, but I know what it is to be burned. I don't think that I would burn anybody no matter how bad they were. If I was big and somebody was bad to me, I would just tell him to go away. Maybe God could think about that.

I'm going to ask her if I can go to church with Janice. Her parents are Italian, so they go to the Italian church.

I can't believe it. I'm going to church. Janice says we can't go upstairs. We have to go to Sunday school. That's all right; at least we're in the church. Why is that lady dressed all in black like that? I don't like her clothes, but she is pretty.

"Hello, Claudette. What parish do your parents go to?"

"I don't know what a parish is."

"Where does your family go to church?"

"My family doesn't go to church, but I'm going to."

"You don't have an Italian name. This church is where the Italians go. You'll have to go where your people belong. You have to go to St. Mary's church on Main Street."

"Yes, Ma'am." I am so sorry that I can't go to church with Janice. I just thought church is "church." Now I have to go all by myself.

Oh my, this place has to be the most beautiful building in the whole world. "Would you tell me where the Sunday school is, please?"... "Yes, I am all alone."... "No, none of my family is coming, but I want to go to Sunday school, please."

At least I know what to call them now. They're nuns.

"How old are you, Claudette?"... "Seven? Then you've made your First Communion already?"

"What's that?"

"You haven't made your First Communion? Then you can't be in this class. This is the Confirmation class."

"Oh hello, Father."... "Claudette, this is Monsignor O'Brien. Claudette is going into the First Communion class."

"How old are you, Claudette?"

"I'm seven, Father."

"You're too old for the First Communion class"... "Put her in the Confirmation class."

"But, Father—"

"Do what I tell you."

Oh no, I'm already a problem. Some of the nuns put their heads together to talk about "the problem." I heard that word "drinking" again.

"All right, Claudette, we have to do what Father said."

Week after week I study my lesson. I memorize every word. Finally it's time to be confirmed. Every inch of me is so excited. I can't stand it. The evening before the big day, we all have to go to Confession. When I go to take my turn going into that box, the nun says, "You can't go in there. You haven't made your First Communion." I'm just as happy not to, because I don't know what or who is in the box, never mind what I should do once I get in there.

The nuns are talking to each other and looking at me and shaking their heads. "Just go home, Claudette, and come back tomorrow." What is wrong?

My goose bumps keep getting goose bumps all day. SHE borrowed a white dress and veil for me. I look like a person who really loves God. I do love God. I just don't understand Him yet.

Janet Barré

The church looks more beautiful than ever today. The flowers are so lovely. The nun explains how we will all walk up to the bishop and kneel in front of him. Then he will slap us on the face, but not hard. The priest comes out and speaks in Latin. Even though I can't understand him, I know he must be saying something wonderful to God.

The music is starting now, and all of the boys and girls stand up to march down the aisle to take communion. This is so wonderful. Here I go!

What is this? There's a hand on me, stopping me from going down the aisle. "You can't take communion. You haven't made your First Communion yet, and you didn't go to Confession. Just sit down until they all come back to their seats."

I want to crawl under the seat and never come out again. Everybody is looking at me sitting here all alone and not marching down the aisle with the other children. They must all be thinking that I have done something so horrible that I'm not worthy. Everyone knows you have to be worthy. I'm so embarrassed; I want to die.

I finally get to make my First Communion. Somebody said they were going over Monsignor O'Brien's head. I tried to picture that. The time comes for me to go into that box and confess. I tell the nun that I don't have to go because I didn't do anything wrong.

Why is she so upset? I'm stabbing Jesus with many

pains? All right, I'll go in the box. I guess I'll have to make something up. "Bless me, Father, for I have sinned. This is my first confession. I swore, and I lied. I only ask pardon of God, penance and absolution of you, Father."

Now I can go to Mass like the big people. I love to go to church and hear the beautiful music and see the lovely stained glass windows. I sit up in front all by myself so that I don't miss anything, although I do wish I could understand Latin. Maybe someday I will. It's very quiet here. I like that. I'm really worried about my family though, especially my baby brother. If they don't go to church, they're all going to die and burn—and he just got here. Maybe God will make an exception. I would. He's just a baby. Hmmm... Uncle Jack's not a baby.

6

A Time For Third Grade

I wish I could make HER happy. Every day she seems to get madder and madder at me. "Just shut up and give the baby his bottle." Everybody in this house is angry. At least SHE's asleep when I get up in the morning. Just give the baby his bottle, change his diaper, drink your coffee, eat your toast, put the baby back in his crib, and go to school.

"My name is Miss Symms. I'm your third grade teacher. Good morning, children."

"Good morning, Miss Symms."

She picks up the chalk, walks over to the blackboard and writes. *Miss Symms.* Yes, she writes; she doesn't print.

Joy! Joy! Joy! We're going to learn to write script.

My daddy has the most beautiful handwriting in the whole world. I don't like to be absent from school; however, there is one good thing about it, I get to watch daddy write my excuse for me. He signs his name like he's drawing a picture. He puts a little wavy line under his name with two other little lines through it. When I get bigger I'm going to do the same thing.

Daddy also prints signs for people. Actually, he does a lot of things. He works in a restaurant, and he works in a factory, and he paints the outside of houses when it's warm, and he paints signs. If you had a store or a business and you needed a sign, my dad could do it for you. I enjoy watching him rule off the paper and then get to work. How does he make each letter so perfect?

I wish daddy would be home all the time so that Uncle Jack wouldn't come here. Uncle Jack only comes in after daddy goes out. I don't think that SHE should be sitting there in just her slip when he's here. You can see her brassier and her girdle through her slip. She loosens her stockings from the garters and rolls them down under her knees. I've never seen Janice's mother or Bobby's mother dressed like that in the house. Actually I don't think that my mother should dress like that. Please don't let anybody come to the door, because it won't make a difference; SHE'll stay just as she is no matter who comes in. Maybe daddy can make a sign for our front door that says, "Stay Away."

We did have a sign on our door from the Health Department when we all had the measles. They did it again when we all had the chicken pox. The sign said that nobody could come to our house until the Health Department said it was safe. I guess Uncle Jack never read those signs. One time daddy made a sign for the teachers at our school. It made me very, very proud.

Miss Symms says that we're going to learn the Palmer method of writing. Would I pass the papers? I'd be thrilled to do that. "Yes, Miss Symms." She asked me to pass the papers. What could make me happier? How I love school!

The school nurse is coming in today. I don't really want to show her my hands when she tells us to, because I bite my fingernails. It's the only way I can keep them clean. I can't take a bath every day as Janice does. What is she looking for in our hair? What are "knits?" I'm glad that's over.

Franklin is just the cutest boy I've ever seen. I think I love him. I've made up my mind that I'm going to do it today, I'm going to do it when I pass the papers. Please, please ask me to pass the papers.

"Claudette, would you pass the papers please."

Prayers really work! Don't rush, Claudette; just take

your time. This is it. I did it. I kissed him on the cheek! Why is he yelling at me that he hates me? That's not the way to treat somebody when they show you that they love you. He's acting as though I did something wrong. This is too embarrassing. I'll never kiss a boy again!

I'm so delighted that our art teacher is coming today. I wish that she could come to our class every day and not just once a week. I'm amazed (this was one of our vocabulary words) at the way she can take a crayon and make a flower come to life on the paper. That's something else that I want to do when I grow up. I want to paint wonderful pictures. Maybe I will. I'll put them all over our house. Hopefully that will help to cover the dirt. Has our house always been so dirty?

It was really dirty last night when Uncle Jack's friends brought him to our house, and he threw up all over the floor where they laid him down. Why didn't they take him to his own house? They said he was drunk. Let's see. *Drunk* (drungk) *adj.* 1. Intoxicated with alcohol to the point of impairment of physical and mental faculties 2. Influenced by intoxication. *Impair* (im-pær) *verb*, To diminish in strength. *Diminish* (Di-min-ish) *verb* 1. To make or become less or smaller... Let's see. He drank so much alcohol that his strength went away so much that he fell down. I adore my dictionary; I don't adore Uncle Jack.

Oh, Miss Symms is taking out her pitch pipe. We're going to sing.

"Claudette, come up here please. I want you to sing the first verse by yourself."

By myself? With my heart thumping, my lips shaking, and my knees knocking who will be able to hear me?... I did it! I really did it. Do other people who sing alone feel this marvelous? "Marvelous." I love that word!

Where did the time go? It's two-thirty, the quiet time of the day—reading hour. *The Cat In Grandfather's House.*

"Yesterday, we left off with Hortense going into the attic. Now just put your heads down on your arms on the desk and relax and listen."

Three-thirty? It can't be! This is so funny. Louise and Bennet are asleep. Wake up!

"Miss Symms, can Louise and I stay after and clean the blackboards and clap the erasers?"

"All right, Claudette."

Surely there isn't a more important job in the school except for ringing the bell. I won't be able to ring the bell until I'm in Sixth Grade.

I know that Louise and I did the very best job of anyone cleaning those blackboards. You don't just erase everything on the board. You have to go back over it with a damp cloth. That's fun! When you wet it, it gets very dark; when it dries, it gets lighter again. Actually, I think that it's gray. They should really call it a "grayboard."

Now we get a chance to push up these big windows and lean way out and clap the erasers together to get the chalk out. They're like a soft cloth. Oh my, the chalk dust is blowing back on us. That's all right. It's worth it, because we got to stay after and help.

I'll walk you home, Louise. Louise has a problem, but I don't know what it is. She always tells me not to come to her door, just call her from the street, and she'll come out. It has something to do with divorce. I looked it up. It means that her parents aren't married any more. I don't understand that. How could your parents not be married? That's what the dictionary said though. I wonder if there are other books that help you to understand the dictionary? If there are, I'll find them.

I hope I don't find Uncle Jack at home before SHE gets back from the Bingo. At least he won't come until daddy goes to work. I better get home fast and get the baby up from his nap. Daddy's working second shift at the factory. I like to say goodbye to him before he goes.

"Goodbye, Daddy."
"Don't upset your mother."
"I won't, Daddy."

7

A Time To Breakdown

"Whose turn is it to go to the store?"

Jouny says, "Robert."

Robert says, "Claudette."

I get chosen this time. I wouldn't mind, but it's so cold, and it's so dark, and it's so far. We used to go down the street to the bottom of the hill. That store was closer. The last time I was there I handed the man HER list and said, "Charge it," as SHE told me to.

He said, "No, I can't give your any more groceries."

I got sick to my stomach. How could I go home without groceries. SHE'd kill me, I *almost* cried. "But SHE said I had to get these things."

He said, "Stay here while I call her." I hear him say,

"This is the last time until you pay your bill."

Now we go to a different store. It's much further away. Also there's a dog at one of the houses that scares me out of my wits. Please, God, please let him be in his house. I put on my leggings, my jacket, my hat, and my gloves, and off I go. I walk down our street, then down West Avenue hill, then by the green garage, then down the dog's street to Conover Street. At least it will be warm and light in the store.

"Hi, Claudette."

"Hi, here's my mother's list and some money, and put the rest on the bill."

"Tell your mother we can't keep putting things on the bill. Next time we can't give you any groceries unless you pay for them."

Oh please, not again. All these people standing here heard him. I'm so embarrassed! I wish I could hide under the counter.

"Here's your groceries, Claudette. Are you going to be able to carry all this? It's pretty heavy."

"I can do it. I'm eight going on nine!" It's so cold and dark out here. I better not cry. My tears will freeze. Let me just put the bag down for a minute on these people's stairs. That's what I can do. I'll just stop at different houses on the way home and rest a little bit. Oh no, one of the bags is ripping!

"Can I help you, little girl?"

"No, Ma'am. Thank you just the same." That cream

looks so good on the top of the milk in the bottle. The street light makes it look even better. It looks shiny. I really shouldn't. I better not—just a sip. I'll take just a sip at the next house where I rest. That is so delicious. Maybe one more sip. Maybe just one more sip. The next time I rest, I'll take just one more sip and that's it. My fingers are so cold.

"What happened to the cream?"

"I don't know; maybe it spilled. Yes, I drank it." I shouldn't have taken it. It wasn't worth the spanking. Daddy said, "Don't upset your mother." SHE's going to be yelling until she leaves for the Bingo. I really do want her to go out, but then the other stuff starts.

As soon as Uncle Jack picks her up to take her to the bingo, I know what's going to happen—first the fighting with my brothers about who's going to do the dishes. There are a lot of dishes. One thing SHE always does is cook supper and Sunday dinner. SHE's a very good cook. I wish she would teach me, but she won't. My oldest sister is married now. There's a pretty picture of her in her bride's dress in the living room over by the telephone. My other sister is out or working, so I don't see her much. That leaves no one to teach me to cook. Oh well, I'm sure there are cookbooks.

Oh please, God. No! There they go! My two big brothers were reading funny books and now they're fighting. I don't know how this happens. Every single solitary night it's the same thing. One says something mean or fresh to the other, and there they go! I can hear myself screaming— STOP! STOP! STOP IT! They're punching, kicking, and scratching each other and knocking over furniture. I can't stand it! Please stop! The baby's crying. I'm screaming at the top of my lungs. I run out the door to the man next door. Please! Please! Help me! My brothers are going to kill each other! Please help me! He runs back to the house with me and pulls them apart and yells at them. He says he's sick of coming over here every night. After he leaves they're too tired to fight any more.

Here they come. Uncle Jack is bringing her home from the Bingo. Now they're going to have their hi-balls. I hate that word.

"Was there any trouble here while I was gone?" SHE looks at my brothers.

"No, Ma'am." Please don't let her look at me. I'll have to tell the truth, and then they'll get me.

"Go to bed."

"Yes, Ma'am." Why doesn't SHE take them to the Bingo with her every night. I'll just take care of the baby and read a book. I'll give the four of them—Uncle Jack, HER, and the two boys—hi-balls when they come home, and I'll go to bed.

SHE's going to have another what?

"That's right," my brother says, "another baby. Why do you think she's getting so fat?"

I have the same old questions: Where are we going to put it? How did it get into her stomach? How will it come out? My dictionary isn't any help. Our bathroom is too crowded now. There's no lock for our bathroom door. Anybody can come in when you're in there. Sometimes when I'm on the toilet my brothers come in and make me stay there while they go to the bathroom. They make me open my legs so that they can go in between, but most of the time they pee on me and then laugh and run downstairs. I can't tell her, because I'll probably get hit for letting them—as if I could stop them! Or else if SHE punishes them, they'll get back at me. God, how much longer do I have to stay here?

In Janice's house they always have toilet paper. I know, because I used their bathroom. I asked to use their bathroom just so I could go in and see how clean it is. We use newspaper for toilet paper a lot of the time, and my brothers sit on the toilet and pick their noses and wipe it on the wall. Every time I go to the bathroom I watch this mucus mountain grow.

Our neighbor two doors down has a different way to get rid of his mucus. He leans out the back window, blows his nose, and snaps it off with his bare finger, throwing it into the air. When the lady downstairs from him complained, he said, "No, I should do like you and blow it into a piece of cloth and carry it around in my pocket all day!"

Let's see. There are ten stairs: One, two, three, four, five, six, seven, eight, nine, ten. One, two, three, four, five, six, seven, eight, nine, ten. One, two, three, four, five, six, seven, eight, nine, ten. I don't know why, but I always have to count everything three times. I even have to sit down and get up three times before I can stay down. When somebody speaks to me, I have to repeat their last word three times to myself. I can't stop it. This is making me crazy. I know how many cracks there are in the sidewalk from our stairs to the street. I know how many spindles there are on our porch. I know how many squares there are in the ceiling in each room of our school. The horror is that I have to count them over and over three times. "Yes, Ma'am." One she can hear, and then two to myself. What is happening to me? I'm exhausted.

At the top of the stairs, going upstairs from the kitchen, on the wall is a crucifix. In the boy's bedroom on the right, facing me as I go into the room, is another crucifix. If I keep going straight I will go through a door to my parents' bedroom, where I will be facing another crucifix.

Back to the top of the stairs I take a left and go down the hall to another bedroom. Straight ahead is another crucifix. If I am at the top of the stairs facing the crucifix I have two to my right and one behind me in the back bedroom. In church we are taught to genuflect in front of a crucifix. Every time I go up the stairs I have to first genuflect to the crucifix in front of me, quickly turning so my back won't be to the crucifix in the back bedroom. Then I have to genuflect to each crucifix in both bedrooms in front of me, and then walk sideways down the hall to genuflect in front of the crucifix in the back bedroom— then go to the bathroom. When I come out of the bathroom, I have to do everything in reverse. The hardest thing is that I have to do this so carefully that no one notices me. No one knows what I go through when SHE sends me up and down, up and down the stairs to get things. I think I'm crazy. I know I'm crazy. Do crazy people cry?

It's another boy.

8

A Time To Explode

I'm going to have Miss Symms again this year. Last year she taught third grade; this year she's teaching fourth. I couldn't be more pleased. I hope she reads *The Cat In Grandfather's House* again. This time I won't get as anxious, because I already know how it ends. I like to know the ending first. I always read the last chapter first, then I can relax while I'm reading because I know where I'm going.

I especially like spelling and vocabulary. My only problem is that I have to keep spelling every word three times in my head. I can't walk on cracks in the sidewalk any more. It's very difficult to walk down our sidewalk now, especially if it's dark. I've memorized every crack and where it is, but sometimes I misstep. It puts me in a panic. I know how many panes are in every window in the school, how many stairs are in every staircase, how many shelves are in the bookcases, and how many steps it takes to get from the doorway to my desk, and from my desk to the lavatory. My brain is about to explode. I try very hard not to look at signs because I have to repeat each word three times and then spell each word separately three times. My whole self is going to blow up. *Now I lay me down to sleep, I pray the Lord I don't wake up.*

I can't stand the filth in the house and the dirty diapers on the stairs off of the kitchen. When I come home from school there is a dirty diaper sitting in the corner of each stair. They're stiff and hard and filled with caca. They have to be taken upstairs and emptied in the toilet—the already nasty toilet. This takes some doing because it's all hard and dry. May I please just live in school?

Miss Symms says that we can make up something special by ourselves for a Christmas program in our class. I'm going to ask two other girls to sing *Oh Little Town of Bethlehem* with me. I'm going to have us harmonize with each other. Somebody told me that the way you harmonize is to have everyone start on a different note. We have these nice little songbooks that the John Hancock Insurance Company sends out to the schools for all the children.

"It's our turn, girls. Let me give you a note. When I say,

'go' we'll all sing."... "Here's your note."... "Here's your note."

And here's my note.

"Go!"

Oh, we must sound so beautiful, like a lovely symphony. (I would realize later that a more accurate description would be a cacophony!)

I can't wait until this afternoon. The children from all the classrooms are going to gather in the front hall. The children from the upper classes are going to sit on the steps of the big winding staircase. It has the most wonderful railing. Wait, I can use my new word, "banister." It has the most wonderful banister. It's a very special privilege to be allowed to polish it. I'll be thrilled when it's my turn.

The sound of all the classes singing together is giving me chills. I feel music in my toes, my fingers, my ankles, my knees, my stomach, my earlobes, my head, and my heart.

"Claudette, come over here, please, and stand up on this chair."

What have I done wrong now? Stand up on the chair where everyone can look at me like they did in church? What now, God?

"Claudette has a very pretty voice, and I hope that she'll be kind enough to sing *Silent Night* for us all by herself."

Janet Barré

Me? Claudette? A very pretty voice? Please let me stop shaking. I would love to sing if I can. Done! Did that sigh of relief come out of me? They're clapping. Everyone is clapping. For me? This is a day of days.

I don't always like to go out at recess when it's so cold. I'm glad Miss Symms let us come back early. I just feel awful for Sheila.

"What's the matter, Sheila? Why are you crying?"

"Nothing's wrong, Miss Symms."

"Claudette, do you have a problem also?"

"No, Miss Symms. May I come up to your desk and talk to you in private?"

"All right, Claudette."

"I know why Sheila is crying. At recess the kids were making fun of her because she's Jewish and she doesn't celebrate Christmas. They told her that she killed Jesus." I know that Jesus had nails in his hands and his feet when he died, and I don't believe for one second that Sheila did it. I don't know who did do it, but I don't believe it was Sheila.

"Come here, Sheila."

Miss Symms really knows how to comfort all of us.

I'm so glad that everybody has gone out. I can take my time and put the icicles on the tree perfectly, all by myself. After I give the baby his bottle, I can just enjoy the quiet. It's really getting crowded in this house. The piles on the refrigerator are getting higher, and we're running out of doors to hang things on. SHE has a skunk fur coat. It's very soft, but it smells nasty like cigarettes.

I wonder where they go on Friday and Saturday night? On Monday, Tuesday, Wednesday, Thursday, and Sunday night Uncle Jack takes HER to the Bingo and then picks her up and comes back here. I know he takes her to the Bingo on Friday and Saturday night, but they don't come back until very late. Why does daddy work day and night?

There's some packages with my name on them. I hope it's something to wear. Even our house looks beautiful with this tree here. I hope daddy likes his presents. That idea Miss Symms had for a pincushion made out of a walnut, some cotton, and cloth was so smart. I'm sure SHE'll like it. I know SHE can use the potholder. Daddy is really going to be surprised with the calendar I made for him. It's good that that man on the street was willing to give me that little blue poppy on a wire for a penny; otherwise, I would have had two presents for HER and only one for daddy. It wouldn't have been even. It has to be even.

Two pair of pajamas for the summer—pink and blue. These are so beautiful, I just can't wait to wear them. Everything smells so good. I'm glad that daddy is going to be home for dinner because he has to carve the turkey. He has to leave right away after he eats, because he works at a restaurant at night as a waiter. That's why he comes home so late. Sometimes I hear him come in about two o'clock in the morning, and I get up and sit with him and talk for awhile.

Occasionally he tells me about when he was a little boy and about Grampa. Grampa was a doctor, and sometimes daddy used to make house calls with him in a horse and buggy. Daddy has a car now with a running board. He must have looked funny in a horse and buggy. He must be very sad that Gramma doesn't want to see him any more. That's his mommy. I wonder why she doesn't like him. Maybe he cried a lot.

Dinner's ready. "Oh please have daddy come to the table right away." The last time he didn't come to the table right away, SHE took a plate and filled it with food except for the peas. SHE said, "He doesn't like peas." Then SHE stood between the dining room and the living room where he was sitting in a chair and threw it at him with all her might. It missed his head and smashed the window. I was terrified. I didn't see him. I just heard the crash.

"Oh God, is he dead?"

"Shut up and sit down. You better not cry. Sit up. Get your elbows off the table and eat."

And eat?? "Yes, Ma'am."

I was really happy when the table got so crowded in the dining room that one person had to sit out at the kitchen table. I always volunteered.

"Goodbye, Daddy. Merry Christmas. Thank you. See you later. May I please be excused from the table?"

"Yes, but leave everything here. Uncle Jack will be here soon. He has to eat."

Here he comes with the brown bottle. Get out the cribbage board. Get out the hi-ball glasses. Why doesn't *HE* just get out!

"Claudette, give Uncle Jack a kiss."

"I have to go to the bathroom!" I'm going to explode. I'm exploding. I exploded... exploded... exploded! EXPLOD-ED... EXPLODED... EXPLODED... E E E, X X X, P P P, L L L, O O O, D D D, E E E, D D D!

9

A Time For War

"My name is Miss Flanagan. M I S S F L A N A G A N. Write it down. I am your Fifth Grade teacher. If you are tardy, you will have to stay after school.

"Why were you tardy, Claudette?"
"I don't know."
"I'll see you after school."
"Yes, Ma'am." I don't want her to be mad at me. I ran as fast as I could. It wasn't my fault that my three-year-old brother wouldn't go to the bathroom, and the one-year-old wouldn't finish his bottle. SHE doesn't get up in the morning when we go to school, but SHE gets really mad if the baby isn't changed and has his bottle, and the

other one isn't fed and put back in his crib until she gets up.

When I come home at lunchtime, I just see her briefly, because she's leaving for the Bingo, and the little ones have to be fed and put back in their cribs before I run back to school. Daddy is home from his morning painting job by then, so he sleeps on the cot in the living room until I get back from school in the afternoon. I can't stay after anymore because I have to get right home for daddy to leave for his factory job. Then I get the babies up and play with them until SHE comes home from Bingo. I hope Miss Flanagan doesn't keep me too long, or I'll be in more trouble.

"You're just saying that. That's not true!"
"Look at her."
"She can't be."
"She is."
"Another one? Where are we going to put it?" More dirty diapers. How many diapers can the stairs hold? Are there going to be two cruddy diapers on each stair instead of one? Why does she do that? Why does she put them there? I don't want to wash out another diaper, and I don't want to fold another diaper! Please, God, I'd rather do without the loaf of bread.

Oh no, we have to be examined. I dread that. I wish the school nurse could examine us. I feel so stupid sitting here in my underwear. Nobody else has a seat that comes down in back. I wish I had a pretty undershirt like Nancy. We look so silly all lined up in our underwear like birds on the telephone wires or clothespins on a clothesline. This paper that they put on the floor is sticking to my feet. I'm so glad that SHE let me take a bath last night, because my feet were so dirty. Why can't we all take baths? We're all as dirty as the house is. At least I wash the babies before they go to bed. I'd really like to put them in the bathtub, but I'd have to heat too much water to carry upstairs. Then there's all that genuflecting that I have to do. I think I've lost a piece of my brain.

Nancy's mother is so beautiful. Nancy must be very proud of her when she comes to school. The mothers are supposed to come to school when their little girls are being examined. Mine didn't come, but I didn't care because it would have been worse to have her here with her cigarette in her mouth.

"My mother said that I can invite you to our house."
"Me?"
"Yes, my mother said the you seemed like a nice girl when she came to school last week. She told Miss Flanagan that you looked immaculate."
Immaculate? Where's my dictionary. *Immaculate* (I-mak-ye-lit) *adj.* 1. Free from sin, stain, or fault: Pure. 2. Impeccably clean. *Impeccable* (Im-pek-a-bel) *adj.*

1. Having no flaws: Perfect 2. Not capable of sin.

Nancy's mother is beautiful, but she obviously isn't Catholic. If she were Catholic she'd know I wasn't immaculate. Besides, the only reason my feet weren't dirty when she saw me was because I was allowed to take a bath the night before I had to be examined. I'm not going to tell her any of this because I want to go to her house.

Look at that unusual car. Daddy's car doesn't have wood on the sides like that. Run out fast before she gets out of the car, and don't let her come near the house. Please, Please, don't let my mother scream or swear until after I leave. You can hear her all the way out on the front walk. Please close her mouth until I leave.

"Give me a kiss before you go."

"Yes, Ma'am." We have to kiss her cheek whenever we go out and whenever we come home. I wonder if SHE ever kisses anybody?

"Magnificent" is the best word to describe Nancy's house. There is a stone wall out in front and a driveway that goes in a circle. The flowers are breathtaking. Lunch is served. Served? I've never seen a dining room table like this or dishes like this or a tablecloth like this or such clean windows with such a glorious view. Her daddy is very, very handsome. He leans over and whispers something to her mother, who turns all red in her face and starts to giggle. He laughs really loud. This is remarkable. They seem to actually like each other.

Fruit cup on lettuce with mayonnaise on top of it? Served by a maid? This has to be what heaven is like. "Yes, I really would like more ice cream, please."... "Thank you."

"You girls may be excused from the table. Claudette, you sit quietly while Nancy practices her piano. Nancy, your daddy and I are going out; however, the maid and the gardener will be here with you. After you're through, you can show Claudette your room."

A light in her closet? I think it's a miracle that she even has a closet. I must be dreaming. You can only see a bedroom like this in a magazine about rich people's houses.

Where is she taking me now? What a beautiful kitchen!

"Claudette, this is Clara, the maid."

"Hi, Clara."

"Open that cellar door for me and go downstairs, Clara. Now!"

"Yes, Miss Nancy."

Nancy slams the door on Clara, locks it, and shuts off the light. Clara is banging on the door and screaming, "Let me out! Let me out!"

"Nancy, why are you doing this to her?"

"Because she's black!"

"What do you mean?"

"Don't you see that her skin is black?"

"So what? Besides it's not black, it's brown. Let her out! If you don't, I will."

She wouldn't, and I did.

"I hate you. You're never coming to my house again." I didn't.

"Claudette, you have all your work done. Will you please take this note to the principal?"

"Yes, Miss Fitzgerald." A lot of the kids are getting mad at me because I always finish my work first. Usually, whoever finishes first gets to deliver notes to the other teachers or gets to help the teacher to correct papers, or gets to be the monitor, or gets to do a lot of things that the other kids don't get to do.

"Teacher's Pet, Teacher's Pet!"

"Sticks and stones will break my bones, but names will never hurt me." That last part is a lie. The names are making me feel like I'm going to throw up.

"Claudette stinks! Claudette stinks!"

"Anybody who touches Claudette's hand when we play dodge ball is going to stink."

"Anybody who chooses Claudette to be on their team stinks!"

"Anybody who talks to Claudette at recess stinks."

They have lookouts posted at the front of school in the

morning, after lunch, and after school. "Here she comes. Everybody hold your nose. Claudette stinks. Teacher's Pet! Teacher's Pet!"

"Make a circle, boys and girls. Jimmy, take Claudette's hand. Jimmy, take Claudette's hand. Alice, take Claudette's hand!! Everyone go back to your seat."

OUR WEEKLY READER, OUR WEEKLY READER, OUR WEEKLY READER. OUR, OUR, OUR... WEEKLY, WEEKLY, WEEKLY... READER, READER, READER... O O O, U U U, R R R, W W W, E E E, E E E, K K K, L L L, Y Y Y, R R R, E E E, A A A, D D D, E E E, R R R.

Sticks and stones will break my bones, names will kill me. Dirt, diapers, Uncle Jack, brothers beating each other up, screaming, swearing, the belt, the miserable messy mucus mountain on the bathroom wall... Wait, that's alliteration!

10

A Time For Terror

"Was Jack here last night, Jouny?"

"No, Dad."

"Robert?"

"No, Dad."

"Claudette?"

Why is he doing this? If I lie to her, I get the belt. If I lie to daddy *for* HER, I won't get the belt *from* her. *Lie* (li) *noun* 1. An untrue statement made deliberately. 2. Falsehood. One of the Ten Commandments. Thou Shalt Not Lie. Is a lie ever not a lie? I don't want to get the strap. I can lie and just go to confession Saturday night and say, "I swore and I lied" because that's what I always say anyway. Daddy, God, and HER. The *boys* just said, "No, Dad."

"Claudette, was Jack here last night?"
"Yes, Daddy."

"Goodbye, Daddy. Don't work too hard."
"You son-of-a-bitch. You little bastard. You're nothing but a sucker for your old man."

She always calls daddy a son-of-a-bitch. That makes sense because he's Gramma's son. Where's my dictionary? *Bitch* (bich) *noun* 1. A female canine. *Canine* (Ka-nin) *adj.* 1. of or relating to a member of the family Canidae, which included dogs, wolves, and foxes. *Bastard* (bas-terd) *noun* An illegitimate child. *Illegitimate* (Il'e'jit'e'mit) *adj.* 1. Against the law. 2. Born out of wedlock. *Wedlock* (wed-lok) *noun,* The state of being married. Gramma and Grampa weren't married when they had daddy, and SHE and daddy weren't married when they had me? Son-of-a-bitch doesn't make sense, because Gramm's not a dog or a wolf or a fox. Where does SHE get these words? SHE always says I'm full of shit. Shit. It's not even in the dictionary. I wonder if she knows that she made up a word.

It's so hot in the house. I'm going to go sit out on the stonewall with my brothers and the other kids. The babies are asleep and besides I can hear them if they start crying. SHE won't be back with him from the Bingo until late. I love to run my hand up the branches of these bushes and have the leaves all come off like a little cup. If you hold it tightly, you can actually put water in there, and it won't leak out. It's fun.

Carmen is up on his porch. I wonder why he just sits alone there every night at the same time. I heard his mom say that he and his brothers all work in the factory. I better not go up the street with the rest of the kids, or I won't be able to hear the babies if they cry. It's so dark tonight. I wish they'd come back right now.

"Hey, Claudette."

"What, Carmen?"

"C'mere"

"What?"

"Come here."

"Okay."

"Sit next to me."

"Okay."

"Just give me your hand and leave it where I put it." It feels like a long rock. What is it? I'm scared. I better not cry.

"You just leave your hand there until I tell you to take it away. That hurts a lot in there. You don't know what it's like."

He's right. At first, I thought it was his dewflinger. But dewflingers aren't like that. Instead of taking my little brother all the way upstairs to pee, we have a little pint bottle in the kitchen. This is how you train him not to wet his pants. If he says he has to go, you put his dewflinger in the bottle and let him pee in the bottle and empty it in the kitchen sink. If you take him all the way upstairs, he might not make it. Dewflingers are only about an inch long and all soft. This can't be a dewflinger.

"It hurts I tell you."

I believe him, but I'm not going to say a word. I feel like I'm going to pee in my pants. If it hurts him so much, why doesn't he take whatever it is out and throw it away?

"If you tell anybody about this, something terrible is going to happen to you. You just make sure you come up here whenever I tell you to."

"Yes, Sir." Dear God, can I please just die now and get it over with? Something else terrible is going to happen to me? There's something else?

What a pretty morning! I love it when the hollyhocks get high like this so I can pick the tops off way up here.

"Claudette, go heat a bottle for the baby and hurry up."

"Yes, Ma'am."… "Here's the bottle."

"Get my teeth on the table."

Oh God, no. I hate this. "Yes, Ma'am. Here—"

"Hand me the baby. You have to go downtown and bring some money to some people. The office is on Main Street. It's number 204. Go to the office upstairs on the right. Here's two dollars. Tell them you're going to bring two dollars a week."

"Yes, Ma'am."

"Give me a kiss on the cheek."

"Yes, Ma'am."

I love to be by myself. The stores have so many tempting things. Someday I'll be a shopper. I like the way that sounds. A shopper. Hmmm... W.T. GRANT... W.T. GRANT... W.T. GRANT... W W W, T T T, GRANT GRANT GRANT, W W W, T T T, G G G, R R R, A A A, N N N, T T T. Keep your eyes on the sidewalk, Claudette, so that you don't see any words. Watch out for that crack. Am I really going to have a baby? Robert peed on me last night and said that's how you get a baby inside of you. Am I getting fat? I just can't have a baby. We're going to have to build another house on to our house. How long does it take to get the baby? Please, please, please, God, don't make me have a baby. I washed myself off fast. Maybe that made the baby go away. They peed on me other times, and I didn't get a baby. I hope this isn't the time!

"Yes, Sir, that's my mother and father's name. Yes, Sir, two dollars, and I'll bring two dollars until it's all paid. How much more? Three dollars? I'll tell them, Sir. Thank you. I'll give them this. What do you call it? A receipt? Yes, sir. Thank you. Goodbye." Why do I feel so nervous? Why do I have to bring money here? They seemed kind of angry.

I like my hair. I'm so glad that SHE didn't make daddy cut it so short this time. SHE always makes me look like the boys. I think I'll run in and see Dr. Strictor and Claudette. I'm glad I have her name. Dr. Strictor said that he delivered me. I don't know what that means, but I know he was there when SHE got me. Maybe he can help me. Oh good, they're home.

"Come in, Claudette."

"I can't stay long. Fritzi won't bite me, will he? He must be hot with all that hair."

"Are you all right, Claudette?"

"I don't know what to do. I can't make my mother like me. I try to do everything right to make her happy, but it doesn't work. Daddy just says, 'Do whatever she tells you to do and don't upset her.' SHE just doesn't like me!"

"You're right, Claudette. She never did. I don't know why not, but that's the way it is, and you're going to have to put up with it. Someday when you grow up, you can leave home."

"I want to be a teacher."

"I'm sure you'll make a wonderful teacher, Claudette."

"Thank you, Dr. Strictor and Mrs. Strictor. I have to go now. I better run."

"He said that I have to send three dollars?"

"That son-of-a-b— is only going to get two dollars a week." He's one, too?

This is the best time of the day. SHE's gone to Bingo, and the boys are in bed, and Robert and Jouny are up the street. I'm going to sing on my "stage" upstairs in the hallway. When I sing, my voice sounds like I'm in a huge empty hall. I don't know quite how to explain it. It's not exactly like an echo, but it sounds bigger than it is, almost like I was singing into a microphone, but not exactly. I'm sure I'll find the right word for it some day. What are some words to express how I feel when I sing? Excited, tingly, stimulated, inspired, thrilled, joyous, happy, delighted. Oh, I'd love to be the person who invented the dictionary! DICTIONARY... DICTIONARY... DICTIONARY... D D D, I I I, C C C, T T T, I I I, O O O, N N N, A A A, R R R, Y Y Y... This is making me insane. Or is the reason that I'm doing this because I am insane? *Insane* (in-san) *adj.* 1. Very foolish 2. Batty 3. Crazy and mad 4. Nuts 5. Looney 6. Screwy.

Well, I've sung every song that I know at least twice. I think I'll go out on the porch and rock and watch the lightening bugs. Everybody keeps talking about the war. From what I can understand, people who live in different countries try to kill each other if they don't agree with each other. I guess my brothers are at war. One of these nights there's going to be more than broken lamps or furniture. I don't understand why they don't get along with each other. Jouny isn't happy at all. He and daddy definitely aren't friends. I don't know what it is. I just know that daddy doesn't make Jouny feel good about himself, and Jouny is always mad at daddy. Daddy always says to him

"Why can't you be more like Billy? Why don't you dress more like him?" That never makes sense to me. We're poor, and Billy's rich; that's why!

Robert isn't happy either. He does very, very well in school. It's a miracle that he's alive to do well in school. One night when SHE was madder than usual, SHE took the hot flat iron that she was ironing Uncle Jack's shirts with and threw it at him. Thank God it missed him. I hid under the table. If her aim gets any better, we're all going to be killed off one by one. The plate SHE threw at daddy with his food on it was a thick heavy restaurant plate. It definitely would have sent him right to heaven if it had hit him, except that they said in church that you have to go to Purgatory first. I don't have any money to light candles for him to get him out, and his mother won't talk to him, never mind light candles, so I'm afraid he'd have to be there for a considerable amount of time. My opinion is that he's suffering enough here without having to worry about more suffering if SHE connects with his head the next time she throws a plate. The same for Robert, even if he pees on me and scares me, I really don't want to see him die from a hot flat iron cracking open his head. I know he got me to burn my hand on the iron when I was smaller, but this wouldn't be even—a burned broken head for a burned finger. My finger hurt, but it got better. If you're dead, you don't get better. God help all of us. Somebody should.

"Hi, Claudette, is Jouny here?"

"Hi, Charlie. No. he's up at the corner with the kids or down at the Green garage. Some of the kids were supposed to meet there tonight to play hide-n-seek."

"Can I come in your house and get some funny books?"

"Sure."

"C'mere, Claudette. What's this?"

"Here I come. What?"

"There's something under the cot. Kneel down and look under there and see if you can tell what it is."

"I don't see anything."

"Get further under."

"There's nothing here. What are you doing? Leave my clothes alone. Stop it!"

"Aw, c'mon. Everybody likes to play doctor."

"There isn't going to be one part of your body that I don't kick and scratch. Explain *that* to your mother."

"Oh brother, there won't be one part of me that won't be smashed if my mother finds out. Don't cry, Claudette. Don't cry."

I hope we don't have an air raid tonight. Those sirens terrify me. I can't believe that the Japanese people are trying to come here to kill us. I got sick all over at the movies when I saw the soldiers take a thing that shoots out flames and sets people on fire. Another friend of ours who came home from the war after he was hurt said that they threw little babies up in the air and caught them on the end of a long knife. I have two babies upstairs that I have to protect from the Japanese; pretty soon, there's going to be another one. This is just too scary. How can I fight off a whole army?

I think that somebody should just talk to them. They must have their own moms and daddies and brothers and sisters and houses and yards. Why would they want to leave all that to come here and hurt me or us? Maybe they didn't think of that. I think I'll write a letter to our government and suggest that. Those airplanes make so much noise. I wonder if it's true that they have bombs in them? Some of the grown-ups were saying that if the Japanese bomb us, then we'll bomb them. If it's not right for Japanese to kill anybody, then why would it be right for Americans to kill anybody. It's like that lying thing. Is it really right to lie depending on who tells you to do it? Is it really right to kill somebody depending on who tells you to do it? I bet that there must be a little Japanese girl sitting on her porch right now with her little brothers in bed, who doesn't want anybody to drop bombs on her either. I think that everybody should just turn around and go home. If they're really that mad at somebody, just write them a letter and tell them so. At least that way no one has to get hurt.

Charlie is a pig. I hate him! He may be four years older than I am, but I'll still punch him. I wish I could tell somebody. I can hear my heart. It's beating so hard that it hurts. I'm so thirsty, but I'm afraid to even get up and go into the house for a drink of water. I wish Jouny and Robert would come home. Well, I wish they'd come home if they're not going to fight. I don't want to see HER come home with Uncle Jack. SHE'll just take her dress off and sit out here in her slip and drink Tom Collins with him for the rest of the night. That's what they like to drink during the summer. He has a big silver cup that he shakes their drinks in. It look like the container that they use at the drugstore to make milkshakes. They sit out here drinking their drinks and smoking their cigarettes until just before daddy comes home.

Oh no! There's Carmen. Please, God, don't let him see me. Please let it be too dark.

"Come over here, Claudette. Now!"

"I have to listen for the babies."

"I said come over here."

Oh thank you, thank you. Here come Jouny and Robert.

"Hi, Carmen."

"Hi, boys, how's it goin'?"

"Great. We've been playing hide-n-seek down at the Green garage."

"Well, take care of your little sister. Now I'm goin' to go sit on my front porch and have a cigarette."

How can that screaming in my head be so loud and

nobody hears it? My skin is breaking! Somebody help me! ME... ME... ME... M M M, E E E.

At least now I can go get a drink of water and go to the bathroom. As a matter of fact, I'm going to bed. That way I won't have to "Kiss Uncle Jack good night" and have him pat my behind with his big fat smelly cigarette hands.

Carmen, Charlie, Uncle Jack—I think my heart is bleeding. Some things bleed when they break!

11

A Time For Joy

It's a boy! Another boy? We already had two boys. Then we got another boy, then another boy, and now another boy. Margaret is getting married soon. She found somebody who loves her very much. She looks happy. I know she'll be happy to leave here. I never saw her much anyway.

The bedrooms are pretty full. The three-year-old and the one-year-old are in with me. Robert and Jouny are together, and SHE and my dad have a crib in their room for the new one. We still have only one bathroom; that hasn't changed. The stairs are groaning with dirty diapers to be picked up and emptied and soaked. The mound of mucus on the bathroom wall keeps growing. There's dirt on top of dirt. The bugs and spiders must be the only ones that are enjoying this.

There is a ray of sunshine in my world. Janice's mother asked me if I would like to go to dancing school with Janice, because she wanted somebody to walk to the studio with her on Saturday morning.

"Please, may I? Please?"

"I'm sorry I can't, Janice, because we can't afford the fifty cents. Tell your mother for me, please."

"You're mom said what? She'll pay for awhile?" I can't believe it! Please let HER say, "Yes."… Well it's okay with HER as long as Robert or Jouny agree to stay home and watch the babies.

How can I possibly get to sleep tonight with all this excitement?

"Oh, Janice, isn't she beautiful. Look at her lovely black hair. We must have the most attractive dancing teacher in the whole world."

"Where are my tap shoes? I don't have any tap shoes."

Wow! Look at all these shoes in this box. That was

really nice of people to leave their old top shoes when they didn't fit them any more. These fit perfectly. Well, look at me! I'm a real tapper!

Sixth Grade and my last year in this school, then I'll be moving on. I really don't want to think about going to junior high school next year, except maybe it will make things better because there will be different kids from other schools. Hopefully, they won't find out about the "Claudette stinks" thing. I don't know how I'm going to get through another year of that. It was so embarrassing when they had the assembly for the whole school, and I had to stay alone in the classroom. The teacher said that they were going to talk to all the children and straighten this matter out. It only made it worse. I have to make Louise stay away from me because the kids are picking on her. She insists on sitting with me under the big tree at recess. Her kindness really touches my heart. However, she has to stop because I can't stand how mean they are being to her. I told her that I'd know that she really wanted to be with me even if she wasn't. I can't let her suffer like that. She doesn't deserve it. She already had enough problems with the "divorce" situation. We will both wait until everyone leaves the schoolyard and then walk home together.

One day she invited me to stop by and visit a woman that she knew who played the organ. She said that she wanted her to hear me sing. We ran there very fast because we both had to get home.

"I've never heard such a beautiful voice."

This can't be true; she's talking about me!

"I play the organ and conduct the choir at St. Mary's church. I want you to sing in the choir."

I can't believe my ears. Me? Sing in the choir? In Latin? I'm trying to conquer English. She's going to teach me Gounod's *Ave Maria*, one of the most extraordinary pieces of music ever written. I've heard it on some of the radio programs that I listen to. There are no words to express how I feel, so I won't try.

"Janice's mother isn't going to be paying for your dancing lessons anymore, so your father is going to have to start paying now."

"I'll ask my daddy."

"You won't have to pay for today's lesson, but you'll have to start paying next week."

"Thank you, Miss Leah."

"Daddy says that he can't afford to pay for my lessons, but he'll paint any kind of signs for you that you might need and he won't charge you. That way we can barter for my lesson."

"I'm sorry, Claudette, I don't really need any signs for anything. I'm sorry."

"Thank you just the same, Miss Leah. I'll put the tap

shoes back in the box."

"Thank you, Claudette."

"You're welcome, Miss Leah."

Don't CRY... CRY... CRY... C C C, R R R, Y Y Y.

"My name is Miss Flanagan. Please copy it from the board on the top of your paper. I am not only your Sixth Grade teacher, but also the principal. All of you were in my sister's class last year, so I know a little bit about each of you already. Under my name, please write your name and address, the name of your mother and father, the names and ages of any brothers and sisters and anything you think I might want to know about you."

"One of the privileges of being a sixth-grader is being able to ring the school bell. However, you have to have excellent grades for me to consider you for this responsibility. Another privilege that you can reach out for is coming in early to do the dusting in the classroom as well as staying after school to clean the blackboards and clap the erasers. The final privilege available to sixth-graders is polishing the banisters in the front hall."

Let them ignore me. Let them not talk to me. I will ring the bell, do the dusting, clean the blackboards, clap the erasers, and polish the banister. I won't have time to cry.

"Now, children, I want you to write a paper on 'What I Did For My Summer Vacation'."

If Marcia writes about going to the White Mountains again, I'll throw up. Every year we have to write this same stupid thing, "What I Did On My Summer Vacation." I guess I have to be honest with myself; I just think it's stupid because I don't have anything to say. I guess after she gets up and reads to us all about her wonderful trip to the White Mountains, I could get up and tell them that I went to the Great Mucus Mountain. "Why it gets bigger and bigger every year!" Let them think about that!!

Songbooks? This is wonderful. We never had songbooks before. We just learned the songs by listening to the teacher and singing it after her. Why is she leaning over each person and putting her ear next to his or her mouth while we're singing? Oh no, she just told Bennett to stop singing.

"You just listen while the others sing, Bennett, because you sing off key."

He must feel so terrible and humiliated. I feel very sorry for him. Don't cry, Bennett. Don't cry. He's crying!

Three babies waiting at home now. At least one is toilet trained. However, the other two are keeping the corners of the stairs well stocked with urine-soaked and feces-filled pieces of cloth. There's nothing I'd rather come home to! Just pick up my treasures on the stairs, go up to the toilet, and start soaking and cleaning and rinsing.

"Claudette, I need your help."

"I'll be right there, Daddy."

"Get the nail polish remover and wipe off any of the paint that's still on my face. We finally finished painting that big house this morning. Careful! Don't get it too close to my eyes."

"It's all off."

"Thank you, Claudette. I have to get ready to go to work now."

"Daddy, all you do is work. You work all morning, all afternoon, and all night. You work every single day. We never see you."

"I have mouths to feed."

If there are so many mouths to feed, then why do we keep getting new ones? Somebody better stop peeing on HER. I should tell her to wash it off fast. It worked for me.

Sunday is going to be the most jubilant day of my life because I am going to sing my solo in church. Imagine me singing the *Ave Maria* in Latin. It's such a glorious song. When I sing it, I almost make myself cry. I'm going to be way up there in the balcony looking out over the congregation. Nobody will know who's singing, because they have to keep their eyes on the priest at the altar. I'll be a secret.

I wish my family were here to listen to me sing. It would have been nice to have at least one of them present. That's all right; God is here. I'll sing for Him.

"All right, Claudette, listen carefully to the introduction and then just sing as we've been rehearsing," she whispered.

The sound of the notes coming out of my mouth astounded even me. That can't be my voice. It's incredible! It's just reverberating throughout the church from the cathedral ceiling, to the stained glass windows, to the wooden pews, to the marble floor, to the altar, to God Himself. I have no need to cry. Every head in the church turned and looked up at me. Surely there will never be another event in my life as joyous as this one.

This filth is making me ill. As soon as everyone is asleep I'm going to go down and wash the kitchen floor. I have to know that something is clean even if it's only for a few hours. I'm just going to sit here on the stairs for awhile and look at this nice clean floor. All too soon every-body will be up, and it will be a disaster again.

Uncle Jack better keep his hands off of me. I hate it when he grabs me when SHE isn't looking. He shouldn't do that. I'm petrified when he comes in before SHE gets back from the Bingo, especially when he's drunk. Maybe tomorrow will be the day when he never comes back again.

"I can't go to church anymore? I have to. I have to sing in the choir."

"You're not interested in church. You're just trying to get out of doing any work in the house!"

"Please let me go. I won't go at eleven o'clock and sing in the choir anymore, but please at least let me go to seven o'clock mass, and I'll be home by the time the baby wakes up. Please!"

"Thank you." I'll sing *Ave Maria* on my stage up in the hallway.

"Yes, Ma'am. I would love to ring the bell! I'll be here on time." Wait until I tell Robert and Jouny that I'm going to ring the bell. They said that I wouldn't be able to do it. I wish that they liked me. Robert has a very nice voice and Jouny does, too. Jouny can sing very, very low. Robert sings up higher. I'm a soprano. Robert is a tenor, and Jouny is a bass. Sometimes we sing together with my sisters out on the porch. The neighbors must think that it sounds nice, because it does. We all harmonize with each other. I'm sure they'd rather hear us singing instead of the other sounds they hear coming from this house.

I love language, but not the kind SHE has. I really wish that there were "bad word" earmuffs that I could wear to block out *certain* words. My brothers are starting to imitate her words. I really don't like that. I'm glad daddy doesn't speak like that. SHE has a very nice singing voice.

Maybe SHE could just sing songs. That would certainly be more pleasant. It seems that that might make her happier. It's hard to be angry while you're singing. Maybe I'll suggest that to her. Maybe I won't. I know I won't. WON'T... WON'T... WON'T... W W W, O O O, N N N, T T T.

12

A Time To Weep

"Pull up your shirt and show them your mole, Claudette. Do you believe where it is? That's going to get a big laugh when she gets older. Smile for everybody, Claudette. Bigger! Isn't that hilarious? She looks like Joe E. Brown. Did you ever see such a big mouth and thick lips?"

How many times is SHE going to do this to me? How many people do I have to show my mole and my big mouth and my thick lips? I wish I were a magician, so I could make my mole and my whole face disappear. At least, at Halloween I can wear a mask.

I can tell that this isn't going to be a good day with

Jouny. He's very, very mad about something. Sometimes he walks in his sleep and scares me half to death. I wish we could be friends, but this is definitely not the day that it's going to start. I better just get away from him.

"Stop pushing me. Why are you hitting me?"

"You're a b—!"

"I'm going to tell HER that you swore."

"Go ahead!"

I never squeal on my brothers, but this time he hurt me so badly. When SHE came home from Bingo, I said, "Jouny swore at me."

"What did he say?"

"B—"

"Get me the strap."

Oh no, SHE's going to beat me.

"Jouny, get in here."

No, please don't hit him either. Why did I say anything?

"Both of you. Get over here!"

My stomach is breaking. SHE grabs Jouny and starts screaming, "I'll teach you not to swear." The belt comes crashing down on him with each word that SHE says.

"I'll (smash) lambaste (smash) you (smash). Does (smash) this (smash) make (smash) you (smash) happy (smash), Claudette? (smash) This (smash) is (smash) what (smash) you (smash) wanted (smash) me (smash) to (smash) do (smash) to (smash) him (smash), right?" (smash)

I was horror struck at what SHE was saying and doing. It was hateful. It was ghastly. It was shocking. It was terrible.

"Please, God, let me go back fifteen minutes in time. Make this never to have happened. Stop Jouny from screaming. Stop her from beating him. How could I have done this horrific thing to my brother?" My mouth and my head are numb. My eyes are dripping and my legs and hands won't move.

"Here. Put the belt away, you goddamned son-of-a-b—. Don't cry, you little b—st—rd, or you'll get the same thing."

Give me the same thing; I deserve the same thing. I would be in less pain if SHE beat me, too.

"Daddy, it was terrible. I can't stand it."

"Just stay out of her way, and don't upset her."

"But, Daddy, I upset her even if I don't upset her."

I know that he doesn't know what to do. He's just as afraid as I am. SHE always says to him when SHE's mad, "You'll have to sleep sometime, you bastard. I'll fix you." Every night I get fearful when he goes to bed that SHE's going to kill him. I hate to look at the butcher knife.

I'm glad that I can go to church. It's so quiet and beautiful. It gives my eyes and my ears a rest; they need a rest. I wish I could sing in the choir again. At least I have my memory of a very glorious day.

"Get my nail polish."

"Yes, Ma'am." I will never wear bright red nail polish and bright red lipstick!

"Get my dress."

"Yes, Ma'am."

"Make sure you're home directly from school. Don't stay anywhere. Get the baby up from his nap and change him and give him a bottle."

"Yes, Ma'am."

"Watch the other two."

"Yes, Ma'am."

"And I don't want any trouble here before I get home."

"No, Ma'am."

I know how to make her happy. I'm going to get the biggest card that I can find, with the biggest orchid on it for her birthday. SHE says she loves orchids, so everybody gets her things with pictures of orchids on them. Surely, this card will make her like me. Daddy gave me money to get the prettiest card in the store. This is the one. I'll wait until everyone is almost finished eating, and then I'll give it to her in front of everyone. SHE's going to be so happy.

I'll hand her the card in the envelope. My heart is racing. I know she'll say it's the most beautiful orchid she's ever seen. I wrote, "For Mother" on the envelope. SHE's taking it out of my hand. She's standing up. She's

NOT taking it out of the envelope. She's ripping it in pieces and throwing it on the floor?

"That's what I think of your card, B—."

I don't think I could cry if I wanted to. I always hear her say to people, "I love all my children the same." Hmmm...

I know she loves Margaret. Margaret ran away once when she was younger. SHE put electric candles in every window, and it wasn't even Christmas. SHE kept crying and worrying and worrying and crying. SHE was absolutely frantic. When Margaret came back, SHE was thrilled. I think SHE likes Margaret's spunk. I'm not spunky. SHE keeps telling me, "You're just like your old man." I don't like to fight and neither does he. I think SHE'd like me better if I started to fight back and swear as the others are starting to do. I guess SHE'll just have to not like me. I hate to fight, and I love things to be peaceful. I don't think I'm in the right place.

What is all this commotion about hidden money? SHE says she's going to tear the house apart until she finds it. They're going up to the attic first. I think SHE's doing everything except ripping up the floorboards. Amazing! They're doing that, too!

There they go marching down the cellar steps. They look like the soldiers on the newsreel going into battle. Whatever is it going to look like when they get through demolishing daddy's work room? There must be a fortune hiding there somewhere, for them to be carrying on this way.

Mercy, here they come, Her with a hammer and a screwdriver in her hand, and the others trailing behind.

"It's in that drawer. He can keep his goddamned key, because I don't need it to open this f— drawer."

Hmmm... Another word I can't find in the dictionary. This is insanity. SHE's smashing the drawer to pieces, while I'm hiding behind the chair because if SHE's this mad now, God only knows what's going to happen next if she doesn't find the money that SHE's convinced is hidden in there. It's not there!!! Stay where you are, Claudette, or you might find a screwdriver going through your eye or have a hammer smash your brain until it looks like oatmeal. Maybe SHE should look at the end of the rainbow!

"I'm so sorry, Daddy." It's two o'clock in the morning, and I know he didn't expect the sight that's facing him. He's just staring and not saying anything.

"Maybe we can fix it, Daddy." (...If there's any kind of glue that can put holes and splinters together.) I feel so sorry for daddy, but I also feel sorry for this beautiful desk. Now it's face is as homely as mine.

Dr. Strictor told me that SHE was engaged to somebody else when she met daddy, and that she came from the "wrong side of the tracks"—whatever that means. Daddy's family was very, very rich and very, very Catholic, and

HER family was very, very poor and very, very Protestant. Being rich can definitely make you more comfortable than being poor. Dr. Strictor said women have "ways" to make men *have* to marry them. Daddy married her. Dr. Strictor said that she thought she would be very rich if she "turned" Catholic because that would make daddy's family like her. Then if SHE was very Catholic and had *a lot* of babies, they would really like her. Grampa started out friendly, but after he died, Gramma could act as she really wanted to. She showed a real aversion to my mother by never having anything to do with my father again. Apparently, he was a disgrace to the family. After the eighth baby, SHE should have figured out that she wasn't going to get any money from Gramma, instead, all SHE could depend on was a loaf of bread from God. No wonder we had to worry and wonder from night to night if the grocer was going to let us have food.

Nobody every mentions the desk. They both act as if it never happened. He hasn't been up in the attic or down in the cellar yet. He always kept his screws and nuts and bolts and nails in glass canning jars. The cellar floor is now on large container for broken glass and the rest of the debris. Broken glass in the cellar, filthy diapers on the first floor and stairs, bugs and mucus upstairs, and ripped-up floor boards in the attic—maybe I can go live in the school or the church or Janice's house. Probably not. She said that the law states that you can't leave home without your parents' permission until you're twenty-one. Purgatory is starting to sound good, except if I kill myself, I won't go to Purgatory; I'll burn in Hell forever. Some choices! Do I want this bad thing or that bad thing or this bad thing?

Good, nobody is in the kitchen. Let me eat the sugar in the sugar bowl and then fill it up again. This always makes me feel better.

Oh my God, here he is! The gray Chrysler, PH 700. Daddy's gone. SHE's not home. Where are Robert and Jouny? Why aren't they here yet? The bathroom—I'll hide in the bathroom.

"Anybody home?"

Why don't we have a key to the front door? "The babies are in bed, and I'm in the bathroom. Jouny and Robert are next door, and they'll be right home." No! No! No! The doorknob is turning. I can smell the whiskey and the cigarettes. No! No! No! Go away. No! No! No! Don't! Stop it! You're spitting in my mouth! No! No! NO! DON'T! PLEEEEEASE!! I'm never going to get up. I'm just going to stay curled up in a little ball on this floor until I die and rot and turn back to dirt. I can't cry.

I won't keep going through this for another ten years until I can leave. I'd rather be dead. What day is it? Monday? Tuesday? My brain doesn't work in this house.

I wonder why my brain works in school?

I have to tell HER! SHE can't hate me so much that SHE'd let him keep on doing these things to me. SHE'll beat him with the belt, and I'll be glad. I won't feel bad like I did with Jouny. I'm happy to squeal on Uncle Jack. I despise him. Sometimes I think about killing him, but then we'd both end up in Hell and he'd still be around me. I really don't want to kill him, I just want him dead. Actually, I really don't care if he's dead, I just want him to stay away from our house. SHE'll tell him to leave and not come back.

"He did what? You lying whore. You slut!"
Stop hitting me. That stings. Somebody stop her. My throat is screaming, but no sounds are coming out.
"You lying son-of-a-b—. Wait until he gets here. You're going to tell him what you said about him."

Why doesn't this floor just swallow me up? Why can't I just disintegrate?

"Tell him!"
I knew that if I told the truth God would protect me. "Yes, you know what you've been doing to me when nobody else is here except the babies."
"You little lying b—. You're just a little sl—t. I ought to smash you right now. Apologize!"

"I'm sorry." Let them have their Tom Collins! I'm going to sit out here on the wall (if Carmen isn't on the porch) until he leaves.

Here comes the liar. I feel the sting as he cracks me across the face with the back of his hand.

"It's not going to do any good to tell her, is it, you whore?"

"No, Sir." SIR... SIR... SIR... S S S, I I I, R R R. It's so dark, I hope I don't step on any of these cracks on the way up the sidewalk.

Whore (Hor) *noun,* A prostitute. *Prostitute* (Pros'-Ti-Toot) *noun,* To offer oneself as a paid sexual partner. *Sexual* (Sek'-shoo-el) *adj.* Relating to the sex organs. *Slut* (Slut) *noun* 1. A slatternly woman 2. A prostitute. *Slatternly* (slat'-ernle) *adj.* An untidy woman.

He's not my partner, and he didn't give me any money. I don't know what sex organs are. I only know what the church organ is. I guess I am untidy. I try to stay as clean as I can. Untidy is messy, and my hair is messy a lot of times because I can't wash it. I guess they're both partly lying and partly telling the truth. I still wish the ground would split open and let me fall in.

SHE's going to have another one? ? ?

13

A Time To Question

Junior High School, homerooms, changing classes, typewriters, art classes, algebra, Latin, what a luscious meal! As a matter of fact, I'd say being in this school is scrumptious, delectable, heavenly (especially Latin), and yummy. I love school. I love to learn. Thank heavens there's a lot of different kids in this class that I don't know. That means that they don't know me. Good! I can start anew.

Roberta is very, very smart. So are Jimmy and Thomas and Gus. I'm not the smartest one in the room anymore. I don't think I like that. The only good thing about it is that I won't be called "Teacher's Pet," although it did make me feel good to know that the teachers like me.

"My name is Miss Burke. I am your homeroom teacher, and I will be your English teacher. Many of my students have kept all of their papers during the year and put them into a notebook. Then at the end of the year, they designed a cover to make a book that they could keep for years and later use to teach their children the things that they learned here about vocabulary, grammar, sentence construction, and analyzing sentences. Perhaps you'd like to do that also."

Would I? I already have a design in my head done in gold on black paper. Why, I'll do it for all my classes. What a treasure that will be to look back on when I'm married and have children. This is exciting!

"Claudette, you have an excellent vocabulary for a young girl."

"Thank you, Miss Burke. I've always loved words and my dictionary."

"I'll be expecting a lot from you."

"Yes, Ma'am." Let's see, there are forty-eight blocks in the ceiling and fifteen panes of glass in each window. It takes six steps to get from my desk to the teacher's desk and twelve steps from my desk to the door. There are four pieces of chalk. CHALK... CHALK... CHALK... C C C, H H H, A A A, L L L, K K K.

"Claudette, did you hear me? I asked you to pass these papers out."

"Yes, Ma'am." MA'AM... MA'AM... MA'AM... M M M, A A A, A A A, M M M.

My art teacher is precious. I can't believe we're going to have an art class three times a week. She's so soft-spoken and kind and patient. Her eyes have little teeny tiny lights that sparkle when she talks and smiles, and I love the way she wears her hair all rolled up around her head. Hmmm... I wonder how she does that. It looks like a great big doughnut made of hair. She's not too much taller than I am. That's cozy.

My math teacher is very strict, but I don't mind it because he's not mean. My typing teacher is mean. I think that she's not happy about something. Well, I'll do my best to cheer her up.

What do you know? We're going to have cooking classes. I finally can learn to cook. Oh, we're going to have sewing classes, first? That makes sense; we have to have sewing first so that we can make an apron to wear in our cooking class. Look at this. I actually made an apron. I would have preferred to have purple rick-rack, but the blue is prettier than the black. What else should I make? I wish that the teacher would make a suggestion instead of saying, "Make whatever you want."

I don't know what I want to make. I'd like to make HER an apron like mine, but SHE might rip it up. I know, I'll make something for my art teacher. She's always so cheerful that she makes my heart smile. I'm so happy that my other teachers let me go to her room if I finish my assignments quickly in their classes.

"Why do I have to go to the nurse?"

"She just wants to talk with you, Claudette."

"What did I do? Am I in trouble?"

"No, no, Claudette, you're not in trouble. Please just go to the nurse's office."

"Yes, Ma'am." My heart is beating so loudly that someone is going to complain about the noise. Why is my tongue drying up? Don't cry, Claudette.

"How are you today, Claudette?"

"Fine, thank you."

"Some of the teachers are concerned about you, and so am I, Claudette. You're very, very thin, and your skin is very pale. Do you eat enough at home?"

"Yes, Ma'am."

"We think that you should see a doctor. Perhaps you're anemic. I want you to tell your mother that I talked to you and that the school feels that you should see a doctor."

"Yes, Ma'am." *Anemic* (Ane-mic) *adj.* Pathological deficiency in the oxygen-carrying material of the blood. I don't have enough oxygen in my blood? I'll just take more deep breaths. I'm not going to tell HER because SHE'll just get mad at me for not breathing right.

What can I sew for Miss Green? Should I make another apron or a pair of pajamas? I think that pink and white striped pajamas would be just splendid. "Pink and White for my Miss Green. They'll make her look just like a queen." Words, rhymes, vocabulary, language, what riches I have. Such a tremendous gift! I wish I could remember the rest of the poem I made up in bed last night. *Hung upon the rough hewn cross, believers' gain and sinners' loss.* What was the rest of it? Why didn't I get up and write it down?

Phooey, I put the placket on the wrong side of the pajama bottoms. Maybe she won't notice. No, I have to tell her because she'll have to put them on backwards. This looks stupid. I'm not ever going to give them to her.

"Just let me see them, Claudette. You don't have to give them to me, just let me see them. Why, they're the most beautiful pajamas I've ever seen. I would just tell anyone who saw them that they were made this way especially for me. Everybody has the placket on the same side. These are an original. Please let me have them. I'm going to a ski lodge during the holidays and I'd love to have them to show them off."

"All right, if you really want them."

How thrilled I would be when she would later tell me how people gasped as she walked down the stairs at the ski lodge in her pink and white pajamas. She had everyone flocking around her asking her where she bought these elegant pajamas.

"Oh, no," she said, "I didn't buy these. One of my special students made them for me."

A "special" student. *Special* (Spesh-el) *adj*. 1. Different from what is ordinary or usual 2. Exceptional 3. Unique and one of a kind. Me, Claudette, special? I feel warm and tingly all over.

"Would you like to come back to my classroom after school and have me work on a drawing with you?"

"I'd love it, Miss Green, but I have to get right home after school because my father has to go to work and I have to watch my little brothers until my mother gets home."

"Oh, does your mother work?"

"No, Ma'am." Please don't let her ask any more questions because I don't want to tell her that SHE's at the bingo. I don't know why, but I just don't want to.

"All right, Claudette, run along, but anytime you're able to, you can stay after with me."

"Thank you, Miss Green." GREEN... GREEN... GREEN... G G G, R R R, E E E, E E E, N N N.

Two big boys and four little boys. Why does God keep sending boys? I think a little girl would be nice. Frankly, I'm sick of any kind of babies. Get them up. Give them bottles. Change their diapers. Go to school. Come back

from school. Give them bottles. Change their diapers.
I'm sick, sick, sick of it all. Why can't I be the one to go to
the hospital and get the baby and bring it back to her?
I'd rather have that job than this one!

"Daddy, I'm so tired."

"I can't talk now, Claudette, I have to go to work. Just
don't provoke your mother. Do whatever she tells you to
do."

"Yes, Daddy."... "Goodbye, Daddy."

"Don't upset your mother."

I upset my mother just by being alive!

Oh God in heaven! There's the gray Chrysler, PH 700.
Here comes the pig. I'm just his little toy now. Quick,
Claudette, up the stairs. Get the chair into the bathroom
and stick it under the doorknob.

"Open this door."

"No, I hate you. You're disgusting and evil and
sickening and nasty and foul and vile, and you stink!"

"Open this door, you b—!"

God, where are you?

"Oh, hi there, Robert. I just came up to use the
bathroom, but your sister is in there. I'll come back up
when you're through, Claudette."

When I'm through with what? Climbing back into my

skin? When I'm through putting my heart back into my chest? When I'm through with this exploding in my brain? Don't cry.

I'm so grateful that Robert came home early. Thank you, God. Robert is a very troubled person. I know that he likes school as much as I do. He's very, very smart, and he has a wonderful voice. If he's in a really good mood, he'll sing duets with me. At one of our school assemblies, he sang the *Rose Of Tralee* and made all of the teachers cry because he sang so beautifully. He doesn't like sports and all the things that other boys like. SHE says very strange things about him that I really don't understand. When SHE talks about him to anyone she usually whispers.

He says that he wants to be a minister. He went to church with a friend of his and decided that he wants to be a Protestant minister. SHE says, "You know we don't have any money for you to go to college."

Robert answers, "Well, maybe if my marks are good enough, I can get a scholarship."

"You'll just go to work like everybody else."

That night in bed I was thinking about the conversation. If you don't have enough money to go to college, or if you don't have enough brains to get a scholarship, then you can't be a minister or, I guess, a priest either. I don't think that's fair, God. I don't mean to be disrespectful, but sometimes it's not a person's fault if they don't have money or a smart brain. Maybe they were just born that way. I believe that you're real, God, but I really don't understand a lot of things about you.

Maybe it's just as well that he can't go to college though, because if he became a Protestant minister he'd end up in Hell. Possibly that's something else You can help me to understand some day—Hell. I asked the nuns why You would burn people, and they told me to go to confession for questioning You. They said I shouldn't ask questions and that I should just believe. I think that if You didn't want us to ask questions, then You shouldn't have given us a brain. And if You wanted us to just believe without thinking, then you should have made us like little wind-up toys with a key in our sides.

I have so many questions about so many things. Why doesn't Uncle Jack go home, and SHE go to bed? He must love it when SHE says "Kiss Uncle Jack good night." I tried to get out of it tonight, but he wouldn't let me. I'll probably dream about gray Chryslers. Tomorrow morning I can escape and go to school. *Escape* (I-SKAP') *verb* 1. To avoid harm 2. To succeed in avoiding punishment 3. Temporary freedom from unpleasant realities. I would say that "escape" is a very appropriate word. WORD... WORD... WORD... W W W, O O O, R R R, D D D. Please let me go to sleep, God.

14

A Time To Give Up As Lost

"He doesn't want the rest of his bottle."

"Don't you come out that room until he finishes every drop."

I've been here for an hour. Why does SHE put so much in the bottles? He never wants that much. Please, please finish so I can get out of this dark room. I don't know why SHE keeps the baby in here in the dark all the time. I'd love to pull the shades up and get some sunshine in the room.

"Is he through?"

"No, Ma'am. He just threw up. He doesn't want it."

"Finish giving him that bottle!"

"Yes, Ma'am." I have an idea. I'll just pour the rest out

of the window. I have to get out of this room, and besides, this is making the baby sick.

"He's all through."

"Put him back in his crib; wash the bottle out."

"Yes, Ma'am."

"Watch your brother in the highchair and don't let him fall out. I'm going to the bathroom."

"Yes, Ma'am."

"Claudette, get up here. What's this on the window sill?"

"I don't know."

"Did you pour that milk out? You did, didn't you, you little b—st—rd? I'm going to break your a— and beat the g—d-d—mned sh—t out of you."

Why am I so bad, God? Why do I do such bad things and make my mother so furious? Daddy said. "Don't provoke your mother," and I disobeyed him, and I lied to her. I wasn't really lying when I said the baby was finished, because when he threw up, he was finished because he couldn't swallow anymore. No, I really lied. I'm a disobedient liar. I'd like to burn that strap when SHE goes out, but SHE'd only find another one. I have to try harder to be better.

Ugh! I despise hearing the mousetrap snap. I know how that little mouse feels. I wonder how long it takes to die? I wonder if he squealed from the pain or the fear because he knew he was trapped? Maybe both. I'm trapped, too, but he gets to die. I can't wait for everybody to go to sleep so that I can go down and eat my sugar. This is fun. I wet the spoon with my tongue and press it into the sugar and then lick off what sticks to the spoon. Please don't let anybody wake up, at least, not until I'm through.

I think I'll go out and sit on the porch by myself for a little while and listen to the silence. This is pure joy—no screaming, no swearing, and no fighting, just pure quiet. I must take a little walk in the grass before I go back to bed. Everybody should do this, just take their shoes off and feel the dew from the grass squish between their toes. The only noise that interferes with the silence is a chorus of crickets. However, that isn't noise, that's beautiful music. Maybe, just maybe, everyone can just keep sleeping like Rip Van Winkle. By the time they all wake up I'll be over twenty-one singing on a stage, painting beautiful pictures, and teaching little children how to fall in love with a dictionary.

Now I lay me down to sleep. I pray the Lord my soul to keep. If I should die before I wake, I pray the Lord my soul to take... Please bless mother and daddy and all my brothers and my sisters and my friends and my art teacher especially. Please may the grocer sell us food tomorrow.

Dear God, I know now that a soul isn't a sole, as I thought, but what is a soul? It's invisible, so you can't see it or touch it or feel it. The priest says that when we die, our soul leaves our body and goes to Purgatory and eventually goes to Heaven to be happy with God forever. Now, how can something that I don't understand make me happy? If you told me that if I was very, very good, I could paint lovely pictures forever and sing beautiful songs forever and eat delicious food forever and have a happy family forever and wear attractive clothing forever and plant wonderful flower gardens forever and talk about how generous you are forever and that I would never have to die and be invisible, that would make me want to be extra obedient to you.

When somebody dies, everybody cries. Maybe You could consider just having us never die. What's wrong with the earth? Why can't we just stay here, and You can keep us young and healthy and come and visit *us*? You might want to think about that. I know You want us to be happy, and most people that I know, I think, would be happier doing that. Practically everyone I know of who is seriously ill calls a doctor, as they did for my Grampa, because they don't want to die. I wish You would consider this. I'm sure everyone I know would be really happy if they knew there weren't going to be any more funerals, except Mr. Landau who owns the funeral home, but I'm sure he could find another job that he would probably like better.

Thy kingdom come, Thy will be done on earth as it is in Heaven. If Your will is going to be done on earth, then why should we leave it? My brain is aching. Good night. I love

You. I'm so sorry that they put nails in Jesus' hands and feet.

"You have to get dressed for school."

"Why, Claudette?"

"Because you're five years old, and five-year-olds have to go to school."

"Watch your brother in the highchair while I prop the bottle for the baby on the cot."

"You sit up to the table and eat your cereal."

"I'll change your diaper in a minute."

"Be quiet while I eat my toast and drink my coffee."

"Don't touch my notebook. If you spill on it you'll ruin my homework."

"I don't know where your shoes are. Where did you put them?"

"Stop! Don't climb up those stairs; you're going to fall."

"You have to go back into your cribs until SHE wakes up."

"Stop crying, I'm going to be late for school."

"Who took my books? I need my history book." The pains in my stomach are terrible.

"Roberta?"

"Present."

"Gus?"

"Present."

"Claudette?"... "Claudette?"

"Here I come. Present." I hope I turned the stove off. I hope the babies don't climb out of their cribs. I think I forgot to wash the bottle out. SHE's going to be furious. "Yes, Miss Burke, I have my homework."

Lunchtime already? "No, I can't walk home with you. I have to get right home and take care of my brothers. I'll see you when I get back. The baby won't finish his bottle, and Philip won't go to the bathroom."

"He has to go or he'll mess his bed."

"I can't wait any longer; I have to get back to school."

"*I* have to go or I'm going to miss my bus to get to the Bingo. Your father will be right home."

"Finish your bottle"..."You must pee, please." Please, Daddy! Please, Daddy! Please get home! I have to get back to school. SCHOOL... SCHOOL... SCHOOL... S S S, C C C, H H H, O O O, O O O, L L L.

"One more second, Claudette, and I'd have to mark you late. Perhaps you should leave home a little earlier instead of always rushing like this."

"Yes, Ma'am." Perhaps I should just leave home period! If I run any faster my heart will burst. My chest hurts so badly.

"Mr. Dexter, come into our classroom and look at some of the handwriting samples the children have given."

"This one is really outstanding, Miss Burke. Who wrote this?"

"Raise your hand, Claudette."

"This is very fine handwriting, Claudette."

"Thank you, Mr. Dexter."

"I'll be expecting the same kind of work in my math class."

"Yes, sir." I'll be perfect in his math class, and I'll be perfect in my English class. I'm going to be perfect in everything. Hmmm... It takes eighteen steps to go to the back of the room down the left side and back to my desk.

There's the bell. "No, I can't walk you home, Louise. I have to get home so my dad can get to work, and I have to get my brothers up from their naps. See you tomorrow."

"Just a minute, Dad, let me put Philip in the highchair. I found the nail polish remover in the living room. Close your eyes. Okay, there's not one spot of paint left on you. You have a long nose.

"I'm sorry that you have such a bad headache. I get them, too. Let me prop the baby's bottle and I'll rub your back a little bit before you leave."

"Leon, you can go out on the porch, but don't go off of it. Take Matthew and let him sit in the rocking chair until I get out there. Goodbye, Dad, I hope you feel better."

"Don't upset your mother."

"I won't."

You kids stay right here. Philip wet his bed, and I have to change his sheets and soak them in the tub. I have to wash out these diapers on the stairs, too, so just sit on the porch until I get downstairs and we'll play a game.

"Where did you come from? Get out of my way. I have to go downstairs. Stop it! Get your hand out of there. Don't spit in my mouth. You make me throw up. I hate that. I hate you!"

"Claudette, Daniel is through with his bottle, and Philip is climbing out of his highchair."

"I'll be right there, Leon."

"Where's Uncle Jack?"

"He had to go to the bathroom. Here I come."

"I'll get you later, you little sl—t!"

"Mommy's home. Mommy's home."

"Be quiet."

"Claudette, why are there dirty diapers left on the steps?"

"I washed most of them, but I didn't have time to do them all."

"Get them washed out."

"Yes, Ma'am."

"Whose turn is it to go to the store?"

"Robert's."

"Well he's not home, so you'll have to go."

"Yes, Ma'am." At least it's warm out. Please don't let them humiliate me again.

"Tell them to 'charge it'."

Oh, no.

Why does he have to be here for supper? He should have to pay my dad for the food he eats.

"Did you disrespect Uncle Jack today?"

"No, Ma'am."

"You lying little b—, you know you did. Apologize!"

"I'm sorry." If I want any skin left on my face and teeth in my mouth, I better not cry. "May I please be excused from the table?"

"Get the dishes off the table and get them washed."

"Yes, Ma'am."

Maybe every mouse that gets caught in the trap doesn't die. Possibly when they open the trap and throw the mouse away, it just looks dead, but actually it's just very wounded. Perhaps it returns to consciousness and then goes on its way to do whatever it is that mice do. Maybe... Possibly... Perhaps...

15

A Time To Run

Why doesn't he leave? I have to get going. I just don't know what to take with me. I wish I could say goodbye to Louise and Miss Green. I'm so glad that I made the pajamas for her. This way she'll have something to remember me by. Claudette, you absolutely, positively cannot cry now. Just hurry up, you two, and drink your Tom Collins and get going. Look at him kissing her out there on the porch. I wonder if he spits in her mouth? I think it's disgusting when people spit on the sidewalk! That man is so vile. I just can't imagine why she wants to be with him. I guess she likes him. Hmmm... Why doesn't she like me? I don't lie to her like he does. I know he's not my father's brother and he's not my mother's brother, so how can he be my uncle? They both have to be lying. I wonder if all the neighbors know that he's not my uncle? That would be mortifying. I bet they do. All the more reason now why I have to leave, because I could never hold my head up again in the neighborhood. Do Jouny and Margaret and Naomi and Robert know? If there was only someone that I could talk to. Good! There he goes. I hope SHE goes to sleep really fast, because there won't be much time before Dad comes home.

Poor Daddy! Who's going to iron his handkerchiefs and shirts and clean the paint off of his face and rub his back when he has his terrible headaches? I'm sorry, Daddy, but I have to go—where I don't know—as long as it's away from here. "Oh, God, I'm very, very afraid, but I'm more afraid to stay in this house."

I'm going to miss going to church. I love the way it feels and smells and looks, especially when the sun streams through the stained glass windows. Someday I'll have a home with enormous stained glass windows. They will be exquisite! Why people will come from all over the world just to admire my windows. Where are my rosary beads? I can't go anywhere without these. What else? Nothing, I guess. Just me and my beads. Wait, my report cards. I have to take my cards.

Be quiet, heart, you're beating too loudly. My breathing sounds like the roaring of the ocean. I should leave a note for my little brothers and tell them that I don't not care about them, I'm just very, very tired. Please be on my side, God, and don't let HER hear me. I can't believe this floor squeaks as much as it does. I sure hope that Jouny doesn't pick tonight to walk in his sleep. Let me get this window open. Goodbye, you disgusting mucus mountain. Oh no, I knocked the toilet paper down. If this roof breaks, I'll be sick. I'm already sick. I'll be sicker. What am I worried about? I've done this a hundred times. Just hang over the edge and shimmy down the post onto the railing like you always do. There! Now jump onto the ground. I don't think I've ever seen it quite this dark. When I went upstairs, it was eleven-thirty, so it must be past midnight by now. I'd better walk very closely to the bushes so that no one sees me. Where should I go? I'll go by my church first and sit on the stairs for awhile and maybe I'll get some ideas.

My footsteps sound so loud; I'd better tiptoe. Just think, all the people in these houses know me, but no one knows I'm leaving. I do believe the whole world is asleep.

Goodbye, Bobby. Goodbye, Joan. Goodbye, Mrs. Murphy. Goodbye, Mrs. Lamb. Goodbye, grocery store. Here I am walking by Louise's house, and she doesn't even know it. She is undoubtedly the best friend a person could ever have. I'll never forget her for the way she stuck by me when the kids were tormenting me. She paid a very big price for being friendly to me.

Here's the church. What do I do now? No. No. No.
There's a policeman walking by the stores. What's he
doing? He must be shaking the doors to see if they're
locked. I'm sure he's not trying to get in. I'm glad this bush
is big enough to hide me. I'm so tired. Why does everything
look so big? My church looks gigantic! I must say, it looks
friendlier during the day. God, I wish you could answer
me. Well, I know you can; I wish you *would*. I really should
have taken a sweater. I didn't know that it would be this
chilly out. Is that policeman ever going to leave the corner?
I wish I had something to read. Wait, I do. I have my report
cards. Look at Daddy's beautiful signature. Daddy could
be passing right by me now on the way home from work.
Nobody's going to be there to get up and talk with him.

Look at that, Fourth Grade. *Claudette has shown
steady progress in all subjects this term. She is accurate in
arithmetic and shows good reasoning ability in solving
problems. She is an excellent speller and does fine work in
English composition. She is cooperative and obeys
commands promptly. Absent eighteen sessions. We are
sorry when Claudette loses time from school. We miss her
when she's absent.*

"Claudette has worked faithfully and achieved a
marked degree of success in all subjects. She has acquired
new work in arithmetic with ease and displays creative
ability in English. She has acquired many facts and given
interesting reports. She does very well in music and has a
sweet voice. She is an eager willing worker and deserves

the high standard she has achieved. She is thoughtful and considerate.

"Absent thirty sessions. We miss her when she is absent. Promoted to Grade Five."

Mr. Policeman, don't you think it's time for you to go home and go to bed? I'm getting colder.

Hmmm... My Fifth Grade teacher certainly wasn't as wordy as my Fourth Grade teacher. *Claudette has done excellent work throughout the whole school year. She has been a good little citizen. Promoted to Sixth Grade.*

Daddy's signature gets prettier and prettier every year. *Claudette has done exceptionally fine work in Sixth Grade. Her arithmetic, reading, spelling, and English are superior; her work in Social Studies is not quite up to the high average in her other lessons. She is pleasant, dependable, and conscientious. With her ability, she will always be expected to do a superior piece of work in every lesson. Claudette is an outstanding member of our group. She is always polite, cooperative, and agreeable. She has done an exceptionally fine piece of work and has done it modestly and easily. I know she will continue to be that fine type of person at Junior High school and will make us all proud of her.*

"B—... Wh—re... Sl—t... Lazy... Liar... F— B—st—rd." There seems to be a very definite difference of opinion here. Well, guess what? I know now what a "bitch" and a "whore" and a "slut" is. I know what "lazy" is. I know what a "liar" is. I know what a "bastard" is, and guess what? I'm not any of those things. I can't find the meaning of f— yet, but I bet when I do, I won't be that either! I don't know what I am, but I do know what I'm not. NOT... NOT... NOT... N N N, O O O, T T T.

Thank God he's leaving. If I stayed behind this bush much longer, I'd fall asleep. I'm glad he didn't hear my teeth chattering. My arms are so cold. I wish I had something to wrap around them. Hi, Dr. Strictor; Hi, Mrs. Strictor. Wouldn't you be stunned if you knew I was walking by your house right not? I'm glad Fritzi's in the house. He scares me when he barks. The YMCA. YMCA... YMCA... YMCA... Y Y Y, M M M, C C C, A A A. I wonder if everybody is asleep up there or if someone is looking out their window? If I walk faster, it will help me to get warm. Oh God, I'm so scared. I better say my rosary. Where am I going to go? Just keep walking, Claudette. Just keep walking. I've never seen the high school at night. I guess I'm never going to see it during the day either, ever again. "I know she will continue to be this fine type of person at Junior High school and will make us all proud of her." I'm sorry, but I won't be able to make anyone proud of me, because I won't be back in school.

My goodness! Look at the huge clock on the Town Hall. I've never seen it lighted like that before. It looks a lot smaller during the day. Left or right? Left. I've never been on these streets before. I'm frightened and cold and tired. Maybe I should just lie down somewhere and go to sleep. No! I have to keep walking. *Hail, Mary, full of grace, the Lord is with thee.* There aren't any more houses. I can't imagine where this road is leading. I think my heart is going to break from beating so hard. It's making more noise than my shoes on the pavement. That must be a lake or a reservoir over there. This is terrifying without any streetlight. I couldn't go back now if I wanted to, because I have no idea where I am. I'd rather die than go back, anyway.

Here comes a car, and there's no place for me to hide. It's slowing down. Just keep walking.
"Hello there, little girl, do you live around here?"
Don't look at him.
"Little girl, are you lost?"
Keep walking.

"Little girl, don't you think it's a little dangerous for you to be out here at this hour of the morning? You must be very cold. Why don't you just get in the car, and we'll stop somewhere and get you something warm to drink?"

Something warm to drink? How inviting that sounds, inasmuch as I'm about to freeze to death.

"Well all right, but then I have to be on my way."

"All right."

I didn't know restaurants stayed open all night. The one daddy works in doesn't. He must be home by now. He'll go to bed, and he won't even know that I'm not there until tomorrow morning.

"Would you like some warm cocoa?"
"Yes, please."
"Where are you coming from?"
"I can't tell you."
"Where are you going?"
"I don't know yet."
"Will you tell me your name?"
"Claudette."
"You must be very tired."
"I'm all right."
"Are you going to sleep somewhere tonight?"
"No, I just have to keep going."
"Would you excuse me for a minute while I call my wife and tell her where I am. She'll be worried if I'm late. I'm on my way home from work."
"I don't mind." It's nice and warm in here, and this cocoa tastes delicious. Maybe I could sleep in here tonight. Well, actually it's morning.
"My wife has a suggestion. She thought that maybe you'd like to come home with us and just stay for the rest of the night. Then, after you have a good night's sleep, you

could have some breakfast and be on your way. What do you think?"

"All right, but I can't stay longer than that."

"Claudette, how nice to have you come and stay with us. We have two little children that you can meet in the morning. Is there anything that I can get for you? Cookies or milk? "

"May I take a bath, please?"

"A bath?"

"Yes, Ma'am, a bath, please."

"Well certainly. Here's some clean towels and face cloths, and here is one of my nightgowns. You'll look very glamorous."

Look at all these towels! We only have one for the whole family. "May I use hot water?"

"Of course, Claudette. I'm going to put some sheets and a blanket on the couch, and this is where you can sleep."

"Thank you. Do you have any papers and a pencil? I want to write about my mother before I go to sleep."

"I'll leave them right on the couch for you."

This bathroom is as clean as Joan's bathroom. Five towels and facecloths! This truly must be what heaven is like. I'd better not use too much water. A black silk night-gown? I'm going to look like a movie star. This is a miracle that these people are being so kind to me. I'll have to write a poem for them in the morning. "Thank you for the paper and pencil."

MY MOTHER. My mother teaches me good things. She teaches me that it's wrong to lie or to steal. She teaches me manners, and she teaches me to speak properly. Sometimes she lets me go to church. I love to pick violets for her. She likes orchids best, but I don't know where to get those. She cooks very delicious food. She also taught me how to say my prayers. Sometimes she brings home cupcakes when she comes back·from Bingo. She also has a nice singing voice.

"Would you like to read what I wrote?"
"If you'd like me to, Claudette."

"That's very, very nice. Maybe my children will write something like that about me someday."
"Would you listen to me say my prayers?"
"I'd be happy to, Claudette."

"Amen."... "Good night."

"Good night, Claudette. Sweet dreams."

I've never smelled such clean fresh sheets and pillowcases. Let me just wrap myself up in this cozy blanket. Dear God, you got me here; now, may I stay here? Please? Good night. Oh, by the way, please help me to get this letter in the mail. Maybe if she reads the nice things I wrote about her, she'll like me, even though she never has to see me again. Thank you. Good night.

I smell bacon cooking.

"Good morning, Claudette. How about some breakfast?"

Bacon? Eggs? It's been many, many years since I saw an egg for breakfast, and orange juice is just something you make if you're sick. Actually about the only time we have oranges is at Thanksgiving and Christmas. "I can stay for another two days? Well, I really need to be going, but let me think about it." Two days with clean sheets, clean towels, a clean house, a mother and father who kiss each other, breakfast, no dirty diapers, no screaming, no hitting, no razor strap, and people who call me by my real name "Claudette," not "B—." There's nothing more that I could ask for, except, may I please have all this forever? Don't be greedy, Claudette, be grateful.

"I gave it a lot of thought, and I've decided that it would probably be all right to stay for two more days, but I really will have to get going after that. Is there anything I can help you with?"... "Just go play?" Am I in some kind of fantasyland? Am I somewhere over the rainbow? Be careful, Claudette! You may run into HER scrounging for that pot of gold. Thank you, God, for my sense of humor. I guess I have to thank HER, too. Some things SHE does are kind of funny, except that they're kind of sick, like when SHE put everything but peas on daddy's plate before she threw it at him and almost killed him. Because as SHE said, "He doesn't like peas. That possibly would be funny in a movie, but the actor wouldn't have to worry about really being murdered. Daddy does.

This is such a lovely house. I think I'll try to memorize it. It's much better than our house. They must have just had it painted, it's such a pure white. The porch runs the whole length of the house, but it doesn't have any spindles or a railing. It just has four pillars. I'd never be able to get off of the roof of that porch without breaking my leg or legs. That's a long way to the ground. The vines all along the roof and coming down the pillars make an attractive frame for the house. The house with the fresh paint, the porch with the pillars. the twinning leaves turning red and yellow above the house make this whole scene look like a painting done by a famous artist. Maybe, just maybe, I'll paint this picture someday. Smell the grass. Look at the flowers. Feel the earth. I love the earth.

"We're going where?"... "Did your mom say it's okay?"... "All right."

"This is where we hide when we want to fool our

parents. They don't know about this cave. Isn't this great?"

"You're very fortunate to have such nice parents. You must love them a lot."

"We love them more than a lot."

"You should. You really should."

"We'd better go back now before our parents start looking for us. Don't tell them about our secret place."

"I won't."

"Would you be upset if I asked if I could take a bath again tonight?"

Of course not? They all take a bath every night? They even put on clean clothes every day? This is truly a dream world. Remember, Claudette, this isn't your world, it's theirs. Just pack up all your pictures in your head because tomorrow you have to move on.

"Are you comfortable, Claudette? Do you want another blanket?"

"I'm fine, thank you. Good night."

"Good night, Claudette."

This is strange. Ever since I've been here I haven't counted anything—not the floorboards or windowpanes or anything. I think my brain is resting. Thank you, God.

That telephone has a loud ring. It's morning already? Look at the dust in that sunbeam. Even dust can be pretty. Wait! He's talking about me. He told my father that he's bringing me back this morning. NO HE'S NOT!!! Quiet, quiet, Claudette. Get your clothes on. Get your rosary beads. Get your report cards. Get your letter to your mother. Get yourself out of here—now! Thank God they're in the kitchen. I can get out this side door. Run, run, run as fast as your legs can carry you. My chest hurts. You can't stop. Get to the cave!

"Claudette, Claudette, where are you? Claudette, Claudette, come back, please, please, Claudette!"

He's getting closer. Don't move. Don't breathe. Stop shaking or he'll hear you. Oh God, he jumped right over me. He really doesn't know this little hole in the ground is here. If I weren't scared out of my wits, I'd laugh. He looked like Superman leaping through the air. Don't move a muscle. I have to move my legs because I'm getting terrible cramps. Don't you dare cry, Claudette!

It's all quiet; they must be gone. Maybe it's a trick, and they're waiting for me to come out. I have to wait longer even if it kills me. My legs are feeling numb. Oh no, bugs! An army of bugs! I have to get out of here—slowly, quietly. Well, I don't know where these woods are going to take me, but I won't go back. BACK... BACK... BACK... B B B, A A A, C C C, K K K.

Why did God make prickers? My legs are bleeding. I really, really want to cry. Good! There's a clearing up ahead. It looks like a big farm. Who are all those men looking at me?

"Hey, Girl. C'mere."

"Hey, Girl. What you doin' here?"

Run, legs, run! How can I run when my legs are turning into jelly? Oh God, I'm terrified. Please help me. Give me wings! Make me fly! Get me back to the road. There it is. Run! Run! Run! This is horrible. There's a car slowing down behind me. Don't look. Just keep going.

"Claudette? Claudette! Get in the car."

"Yes, officer. Is my mother here?"

"No, but your father is here."

"May I please see him?"

"Not yet. We have to talk to you. What you did is a very, very serious thing. Nothing can be so bad that you have to run away from home. We're warning you that if you do this again, you will be sent to a reform school for delinquent girls. Until you're twenty-one years old, you will obey your parents and not make any trouble for them. Am I making myself clear?"

"Yes, sir."

"All right, your father is outside to take you home."

"I'm sorry, Daddy."

"I know you are, but when you get home, don't upset your mother. Just do whatever she tells you to do, and don't make her angry."

"Yes, Daddy. I have a story that I wrote about her; would you give it to her?"

"Hello, Mother."
"Tell the b— to get upstairs and get the baby."
"Do what your mother says, Claudette."
"Yes, sir." Home sweet home. HOME... HOME... HOME... H H H, O O O, M M M, E E E.

16

A Time To Wail

"Tell us a story, Claudette."

"All right. Here, little one, sit on my lap. The rest of you sit on the floor. *Once upon a time...*"

"Claudette, you tell the best stories."

"Go out and sit on the porch, and I'll be right out. I have to go to the bathroom." Something is very wrong here. Oh my God, I'm covered with blood! What's bleeding? Where am I bleeding? What's happening to me? I can't stand up. Blood is just running out of me. Am I dying? Somebody help me! What should I do? Should I go to Dr. Strictor? That's a couple of miles away, and I'll have to take the four children with me. Oh, God, please help me.

"Claudette, are you upstairs? The baby is climbing out of the highchair. You'd better get down here. Mother would kill you if she knew you left them alone."

Should I tell him? This is dreadful. "Jouny, I think I'm dying. I'm covered with blood, and I don't where it's coming from."

"You'd better call mother."

"I don't know where she is." She's probably at Flossie's with Uncle Jack.

"Flossie, this is Claudette; is my mother there, please?"

"What do you want?"

"I don't know. Jouny said I should call you. I'm bleeding, and I don't know from where. I stuffed myself with toilet paper, but it's not stopping. I can't move."

"In back of the bathtub is a blue box. Take one of the things out. The long end goes in back. Now get off the phone."

What in heavens name is going on? Am I going to die? Did this happen to Jouny and Robert? Is that how he knew I had to call HER? I don't have any other underwear. I'll just have to wash these and put them back on wet. Why do I feel so ashamed and embarrassed?

"Stop crying, I'll be right down and play with you."... "Please don't leave, Jouny"... "All right, goodbye, but I wish you'd stay with me."

Oh God, there's blood all over the chair. Let me clean it before SHE gets home. My legs don't need any more tastes of the strap. I want to cry, bawl, wail, and yell, but I won't.

I really wish that I could go out and sit on the front wall. I miss it. Carmen stole this happiness from me. At least, if I'm not there, he can't make me come up on the porch. Here THEY come. Get out the highball glasses. I'm going to bed.

"All right, get dressed, you two, or you'll be late for school. Finish your cereal after you get dressed."... "You, stay in the highchair while I fix my hair."... "Don't touch my coffee. Put it down."... "Okay, let's change your diaper and back you go into the crib until SHE gets up. Yes, you have to go back to bed, too, until SHE gets up. Finish your cereal, and let's go."... "I don't know where you put your shoes. Look for them!"... "Don't cry. You kids are making me crazy!! Lie down, both of you. I'll be back at lunchtime."... "Let's go, Matthew, Leon, I'll walk you part of the way."

"Good morning, Claudette, I understand that you went on a little adventure."

"Yes, Miss Green, I did something very, very serious, but I'm going to be better." I love the way it feels when she puts her arm around me; she smells luscious.

"Claudette, any time you want to come into my class and work on a project, you may, even if there are children here from another class. Also any afternoon after school, if you want, you can come in and talk. I'm always here for a while."

"Thank you, Miss Green, but I have to get home immediately after school. I have responsibilities." I wonder why she's being so nice to someone who did such a serious thing? Yes, I really love the way she smells.

This is so satisfying—making these notebooks from all my classes. I'm really pleased with the designs I made for the covers, and someday I'll show all of them to my children. I especially enjoy analyzing sentences. I especially, especially enjoy seeing all these "A's" and "100's" on my papers. I'll bet I'm going to get a perfect report card. Surely, that will make HER like me.

"Did you get your report card today?"

"Yes, Ma'am. I got all A's, and an A+ in math."

"Of course you did; you're my daughter. Go tell your father to sign it."

"Yes, Ma'am."

"Get the kids in bed before you go back to school and make sure you put Daniel on the toilet so that he doesn't mess his bed. I'm going to the Bingo. Don't leave until your father gets home. If you have to be late, you'll have to be late."

"Yes, Ma'am."

"Leon, Matthew, you two get going now so that you're not late. Philip, you stay on the chair while I put Daniel on the toilet."

I can't believe I can't train this child. "Please go. I have to get back to school. I don't want to come home to a mess. Please, you know you have to go." These stomach pains are killing me. You won't go? Well I have to put you in the crib. You've managed to outdo me every day, but today you won't. I'm going to put pins all along the bottom of this bunting and pin the bottom of your sleeves. I don't know how you got out of it yesterday when I sewed you in, but today you won't be able to make your vile sickening mess!

This is so great. I learn as much about English in my Latin class as I do in my English class. Mr. Byrd—his name really suits him. He looks like a little bird. He's not much taller than I am either. I wonder if that bothers him. I know the kids always pick on anybody who's short. I bet he dreaded being short. He must know that they call him old shorty bald head. I like his "thinking" look. His eyes go up and to the right, and they sort of smile a little. Sometimes they match the tiny smile on his face. It's rarely a big smile, but it's definitely a smile. The only time he really laughed was the day he translated "Caesar brought her wine and nectar." He and the other teachers that were in the room laughed their heads off, and Mr. Byrd's face got all red. I still don't know what the joke was.

"No, Miss Green, I can't come after school to work on the portrait. I have to get right home to take care of my brothers so that my dad can go to work.".... "Yes, I'm really happy with the way the picture's turning out. I didn't think I'd like working with charcoal, but I'm really enjoying it. If I finish my math assignment early tomorrow, I know Mr. Davies will let me leave his class to come here and let me work on it. He said that I can do that anytime I want to. Miss Burke said the same thing. I really appreciate them for letting me do that. I love my art class. I'll see you tomorrow."

"What's the matter, Daddy? Do you have another one of those terrible headaches?".... "I'll get a cold cloth to put over your eyes, and I'll rub your feet. Maybe that will help. Why don't you stay home from work tonight? You already worked all morning.".... "Does that feel good?".... "Okay, if you have to go, you have to go. Call me when you're ready for me to get the polish remover, and I'll take the paint off. I'm going to go upstairs and see if Daniel is awake."

Please God, please dear God, please, dear God, make it so that it didn't happen again today. I can't stand it any more. I hate to come up these stairs and do all of this genuflecting. I'm going insane. No! No! No! I can smell it out here. I can't go through that door again. "Daddy! Come here and look at him. I can't clean this up one more time. I had him on the toilet for at least a half hour, and he just wouldn't go before I went back to school. Every day I have this. Look at him! He has caca in his hair and his ears, under his fingernails, between his toes, all over his stomach, and look! He has it on every single spindle on the crib, and the blanket, and the sheet, and on the wall. No matter what I do, he gets out of that bunting. I want to scream and scream and scream until I rip my throat out!!!"

"Just do what you have to do and get him cleaned up before your mother gets home. I have to go to work."

"Yes, Sir."... "By the way, Daddy, remember the letter that I wrote about mom when I ran away? Did you ever give it to her, as I asked you do?"... "She didn't read it?"... "She just tore it up?"... "Okay."

Where do I start? Go down and heat the water to put in the bathtub. "Leon, Matthew, why are you late getting home? Change your clothes and sit down until I finish cleaning Daniel and his bed." How does he manage to do this? It's so disgusting! This has been going on for over a year. How am I going to keep on dealing with this? My nostrils are rotting. I really do have to put my hands in all of that putrid mess everyday—everyday! Even the janitor gets a holiday. "Into the tub with you."

"Claudette, what are the boys doing down here alone?

Get down here!"

"I haven't finished cleaning the mess off of the walls and the crib from Daniel."

"You son-of-a-b—, didn't I tell you not to leave for school until he went. He has to be trained!"

"The teacher said that I can't keep being late."

"Tell that f—ing teacher I said you have responsibilities."

"They told me again that I have to see a doctor because I don't look right."

"You tell them that I said to mind their own g—d-d—mned business. I'll decide if you need a doctor, and you don't!"

"Yes, Ma'am."

"Get that crib cleaned and get down here and get to the store to pick up this stuff for supper."

"Yes, Ma'am." Dear God, I'm so very, very tired. I'm starting to have trouble remembering what day it is. What day is it?

"This stew is very delicious."

"Shut up and eat."

"I'm finished. Could Robert watch the boys after school tomorrow, because I've got to finish my painting in art class?" Oh God, why does SHE have to slap me across the face like that? SHE almost knocked me off of my chair. Now what did I do?

"Would you like to repeat that sentence, you little b—?

You don't say 'I've got to finish my painting,' you say 'I have to finish my painting'."

As long as I'm around HER, I'll always get an *A+* in grammar. If they marked you for manners, I'd get an *A+* in that, too. If you forget and put your elbows on the table, you'll find yourself knocked down on the floor and never know what hit you. I appreciate knowing how to speak and act, but for now SHE gets an *F* in teaching ability. My face hurts. I hope I don't have a black eye. We don't need two of us looking like that.

Look at poor Philip's eye. He should have just let HER wash his hair and not make a fuss. SHE knows he gets scared when SHE washes his hair. I don't blame him. It stings when SHE lets all that soap get in his eyes. It's too bad his hair got so long. If it didn't have to be cut, SHE wouldn't have been washing it. I wish I hadn't walked in when I did, then I wouldn't have to have the sight of all that blood in my memory bank. The sound of HER smashing his head against the faucet was enough without seeing that blood gushing all over. I wonder if daddy will lie as SHE told him to.

"Tell the doctor and the barber that he fell down the stairs."

This woman is pathetic. I'll rock Philip and tell him an extra story when he gets home.

I thought growing up would be fun. It just gets harder and harder. At least some of the work has been cut down.

Those kitchen cabinets were so pretty when we first moved here, with their little glass squares. We still have squares, but no glass. There's no point in replacing it, it just challenges HER to break some more. I thought that if you could always have your own way, that things would be wonderful. However, I'm not so sure now, because everybody does whatever SHE wants, but it doesn't seem to make HER happy. I wonder what the problem is!

"Claudette, you did a superb job on your charcoal portrait. Also, I hung your watercolor of the boats in the hallway. Both pieces of work are beautiful!"

Even the hair on my ears is tingling. I'm so proud. "Thank you, Miss Green. At the end of the year I'm going to take all of my work and all of my art projects and put them carefully away in our attic. Can you imagine how many treasures I'm going to have to show to my children by the time I finish high school?"

"You certainly will, Claudette. Did you talk to your mother about seeing the doctor? You look very pale."

"I did. She said she'd take care of it." Somehow I don't think Miss Green would like to hear the rest of HER message.

I'm so nervous about going to Confession Saturday. I can't imagine what's going to happen to me when I tell the priest that I stole my sister's bra. Actually, I just borrowed it; but, in that I didn't tell her, I think that's really stealing. I'll see what the priest says.

"Bless me, Father, for I have sinned. It's been one week since my last confession. I swore and I lied..."

"And?"

"Uh, nothing, Father. I swore and I lied." I can't tell him this. I'll just have to settle this with God. What was I to do, God? I needed some kind of covering, because all the kids are making fun of me. You know I couldn't ask HER, so when we were at Margaret's house, I looked in her drawer and I took a bra, because she had a lot of them. I'm sure she would have given it to me, but I was too embarrassed to ask. When I get big enough to get a job, I'll buy another one and put this one back. Growing up is certainly involved.

I should send my story to READER'S DIGEST about what happened during the summer."

Dear Readers Digest, here's my story:

This summer like every other summer, I got a very, very bad sunburn. I do it deliberately because everybody always looks at me and goes "ugh" because I'm so white. No matter how long I stay in the sun, I don't tan, but I do burn. At least that way I have some color—red. Of course, the pain is terrible so when I went to bed, I couldn't put any pajamas on. I just slept with a sheet over me, flat on my back. In the morning I overslept, and my mother yelled at my seven-year-old brother to wake me up to feed the baby. He ran into the room and pulled the sheet off. Of course, I was as naked as a jay bird, and I am a teenager now. He looked at me horrified and ran from the room screaming, "Mommy, Mommy, Claudette's sunburn is so bad, her chest is all swollen."

I hope you'll print my story; I need the money.

17

A Time To Explode

Dear God, if you won't stop sending babies, could you at least please stop sending boys? I can't take care of the four we have now. Just forget the loaf of bread, I'll bake my own.

"This is the hospital calling. I'd like to inform you that your mother had a baby boy."

No! No! No! I have enough tears inside of me to make another ocean.

Gray Chrysler, PH 700. That pig is trying to be my bra. I wish I could cut his hands off. Even if I told Dad, he wouldn't do anything, and SHE doesn't believe me. I promise you, God, that if I have any little girls, I'll never let anyone hurt them like this. Here they come with the new baby. Why is he here? More bottles, more diapers, more filth. It's so dirty here now, we have bugs. That big barrel over by the stove makes me want to vomit. When I saw those maggots in there yesterday, it horrified me. That garbage barrel should be cleaned out. What if they crawl out of there and get on the floor and walls? They look like slimy elbow macaroni. Tonight, when everybody goes to sleep, I'm going to wash my sheets and put them on the line outside. I'll get up early and put them back on my bed.

I have such a dilemma with my underwear and my socks; they smell so badly. I have to think of something else. I thought my idea of hanging them out of the window at night to air out was a good one until it rained last night. It was miserable putting on wet socks and underwear. As soon as the heat goes on, I can wash them and put them on top of the register on the floor behind the bath-tub. The heat from the furnace will dry them at least. Until then, I'll have to just keep hanging them out the window and pray that it doesn't rain. I'll die if anybody sees the bra.

"You want me to introduce the speakers?"... "I'd be honored."

"Dad, they're going to have a special program in school

and they asked me to be the announcer and introduce all the speakers. They even asked me if I would sing a song. Could you please ask mom if I could get something pretty to wear, like maybe a nice blouse? Everybody is going to be looking at me."

"Just because she said 'no,' don't make a fuss now. Don't upset your mother."

"Yes, sir."... "Come on boys let's take a walk over to the cleaners. We'll pick some flowers and weeds on the way back. Weeds can be very pretty, too." I like Leroy and Sylvia. I'm very glad they opened this little dry cleaning store. They're both nice to talk to. I wonder if they ever go a day without kissing. They just kiss, kiss, kiss. KISS... KISS... KISS... K K K, I I I, S S S, S S S.

He said they've been married six months. She said, "Six months and five days." He said, "Well, excuse me."

She must have, because she kissed him again. I like to be around them. They said that when I'm old enough I can work for them. I wonder where you go to buy a bra? Maybe I can get up my nerve to ask Sylvia.

"Hi, Claudette, you look kind of sad."

"Actually, something nice happened today. The teacher asked me to be the announcer for a special program, and they want me to sing a solo."

"You must be so excited."

"I don't know if I'll do it, because the kids always make

fun of my clothes. I think I'll just tell her I'll do it another time. I have to go now, Sylvia. Boys, tell Sylvia goodbye."

"Goodbye, Sylvia."

"Wait a minute, Claudette. I've been trying to remember to ask you about this, and I always forget. There's a pretty skirt and blouse that a customer forgot to pick up, and it's just about your size. I called her, and she said she didn't want it. Let me run into the back and get it."

"It's beautiful. Look at the little monkeys on it."

"I think it will fit, Claudette, what do you think?"

"I think I'll make it fit!!"

"Thank you so much, Sylvia. Thank you, Leroy." I'm so happy, I could fly. "C'mon, boys."

"Why are you out begging, you little b—."

"I didn't beg; she offered it to me."

"Get upstairs and get the baby. He has to have a bottle."

"Yes, Ma'am." BOTTLE... BOTTLE... BOTTLE... B B B, O O O, T T T, T T T, L L L, E E E. Genuflect, Claudette. Ten stairs up, ten stairs down.

"Here's the list. Get to the store and get back here in a hurry. The Bingo's starting early tonight."

"All right, get the dishes off the table. You get the kids

in bed and get the dishes done before you start your homework."

Put five kids to bed. Wash dishes for ten people? Maybe reform school isn't as bad as they say. "I don't feel very well."

"Shut your g—d-d—mned mouth and get busy. You're just like your old man. He's a big fake with his supposed headaches. You're just like him. You don't feel well. You're just trying to get out of doing your work. Now get busy, or I'll break your a—."

"Yes, Ma'am."

"And you'd better not cry, you son-of-a-b—. Do you hear me?"

"Yes, Ma'am." Do I hear her screaming in my eardrums? Please go to your Bingo. BINGO... BINGO... BINGO... B B B, I I I, N N N, G G G, O O O. That's her lingo. As for me, I think I'll sing-o.

"Come on, boys. Line up so I can get you ready for bed." ..."You have to say your prayers."

"Why?"

"Because."

"Because why?"

"Because you have to learn to talk to God."

"Who's God?"

"We'll talk about it tomorrow."

"Are you our mother, Claudette?"

"You know I'm not."

"Can I call you mommy?"

"Sure, but I don't think you better let HER hear you."

"Kiss."... "Good night, Matthew. Good night, boys."

"Good night, Claudette."

"No fighting. I'm going to sing a few songs on my stage in the hallway. I'll sing you to sleep."

"Tell us a story, Claudette."

"No, I'm going to sing."

"Who's downstairs? Jouny? Robert? Who's down there?"

"I thought you took my mother to Bingo."

"I did, and I'm going to stay here until I have to go get her. You have to get down here and do the dishes and get your homework done, so you better come down now."

"No!" Oh God, what can I do? I won't go down there. There's a ton of dishes though, and I won't be able to get them all done in the time it takes him to go and get her; and I'll be in trouble in school if I don't have my homework done. Babies, homework, dishes, screaming, "Uncle" Jack. No more, no more, no more. Who cares? Who cares? Who cares? I'm so dizzy, I feel like I'm going to fall over. "Leon, Matthew, move over. I'm going to lie down with you for a while." I can hear the pig breathing at the bottom of the stairs. I can smell him all the way up here.

"Okay boys, *Once upon a time...*"

"I'm sorry that I couldn't finish my homework last night. I didn't feel well."

"All right, Claudette, but you know you need an excuse from home."

"Yes, Ma'am. I'll ask my dad." Why do I think SHE wouldn't write an excuse for me? SHE half killed me when SHE dragged me out of bed last night to do the dishes. This is a pitiful person.

"Claudette, your skirt and blouse are so pretty. You look very nice. I'm sure you'll sing as pretty as you look."

"Thank you."

"And now to end our program, I'm going to sing *You'll Never Walk Alone.*" This is so thrilling. They're clapping for me!

I have to apologize to my blue pajamas tonight because I'm wearing the pink ones. I forgot to apologize to the clothespins when I took the diapers off the line because I didn't put them back in the bag. What is happening to me? What day is it? Is this today's paper? It can't be; it says "Thursday," but yesterday was Monday. Don't cry. Don't cry. Don't cry. Somebody please help me. I can't breathe. I'm drowning. I'm burning. I'm suffocating.

"Claudette! Claudette! Get up and get the baby a bottle."

"Yes, Ma'am."

"It's too hot! Go cool it off!"

"Yes, Ma'am."

"Get a move on, b—!"

"Yes, Ma'am." Please, no more. No more what? I don't even know. No more waking up in the mornings? I don't know. I'm very tired—very tired.

I'm glad it's cold now. At least the furnace is on, and I can wash my socks and underpants and Margaret's bra. I love Christmastime. Even our house looks pretty if you just look at our windows. Why you can see this beautiful tree from across the street, and the candles in the windows look so cozy. I'm glad that everyone is out. Now I can put the icicles on the tree myself. Nobody puts them on as straight as I do. There is no music in this world, in the universe, that is as beautiful as Christmas music. Well, maybe the angels make more beautiful music, I don't know; but this is glorious, magnificent! It must have been dreadful when people didn't have radios. That would be awful—not to be able to hear orchestras and choruses. I can't imagine a world without music. Oh phooey, it's getting all staticky. What's he saying?

The guns are all quiet. The boys on both sides are singing Christmas carols.

They must be so sad, so far from home. Their families must be just as sad.

God, I just don't understand you. I need some explanations. I want to know who you are, but you make things very complicated. In church they tell us to pray for "our boys" in the war. However, I learned in school that there are Catholic and Protestant and Jewish people living in Germany and Italy just like here in our country. The man on the radio just said the guns are quiet, and the boys on both sides are singing Christmas carols. If they don't have to kill each other today, why do they have to kill each other tomorrow, especially if they have the same religion? Aren't the Catholic, Protestant, and Jewish mothers in Germany praying for their boys to win just as the Catholic, Protestant, and Jewish mothers here are praying for their sons to win? Who's side are you on? And why are you on anybody's side, when they're going to the same churches? I've talked to you about the soul before. I'm still waiting for more information, and how about Hellfire? People get upset when they see soldiers in the newsreels using flame throwers to set their enemies on fire, yet I'm supposed to believe that you burn people forever. To me, the punishment doesn't fit the crime. At least, only burn them an equal amount of time that they were bad. If I live a bad life for seventy-five years, then burn me for seventy-five years, not forever. Personally, I don't think you should burn people at all. I think we've talked about this before. I don't like it when the soldiers do it with their flame throwers, and I don't like it if you do it either. I really want to know you more and understand you better, yet I don't know how you're going to accomplish that, if at all. I'm going to ask the priest the same questions that I asked you. This is how I feel, that I have the right to ask you, and that you are obliged to answer, otherwise you shouldn't have designed me with a brain. Please excuse me if I sound disrespectful again.

"Father, I have a lot of questions."... "Go to Confession and say what?"... "Yes, Father."... "Bless me, Father, for I have sinned. It has been one week since my last confession. I swore and I lied, and I asked too many questions. I have too little faith. I only ask pardon of God, penance and absolution of you, Father."

Please, Claudette, this is your brain talking. Please, no more! Don't think! Don't feel! JUST YIELD!

18

A Time To Die

I've become quite proficient at disconnecting myself at home. If I stay connected, I'll be swallowed up. I've become an observer and not a participant. If I become a participant, it will make me a partner in this heinous behavior being perpetrated on me. *Heinous* (Ha-nes) *adj.* Abominably wicked. If I remain an observer I can survive. To really accept that I am this unloved and unlovable is completely intolerable in my struggle to continue to exist. Heinous behavior truly is abominably wicked. I'm forced to observe it, however, I WILL NOT PARTICIPATE!

Finally, I'm in high school. How will I ever find my way around? There's an overwhelming number of stairs and doors and windows and desks and ceiling panels here to count. My brain is going to implode. I love the way school smells when we come back from summer vacation. The janitors have certainly been working hard. The newly polished wooden floors have their own special scent. Every window is so clean, they look as though they have no glass in them. These desks are really neat. I wonder who all these people are who carved their names here. I'd be scared to death to do that. Maybe one of them will be president some day, and maybe one of them will write a book.

This is so different. I get to pick out some of the classes I prefer to take. Music—first period every morning? Could there be a better way to start the day? I love it here!

I think the gray skirt and yellow sweater that I bought for school looks really nice. I've figured out a way to make it look different. One day I'll button my sweater all the way up the front. Every other day I'll unbutton the two top buttons and button the second one inside out. That way, the sweater looks like it has a V-neck.

How kind of Joyce to show me how to do this. She asked me, "Why don't you ever wear anything different?" And I said, "Because I don't have anything different." So she redesigned my outfit. Every now and then she brings in a scarf for me to wear on my sweater. It really gives me a whole new look. She must have said something to the other girls, because every once in a while one of them brings something for me to wear for the day. Of course, I have to give it back at the end of the day, but I really appreciate it.

This morning I know that I experienced a miracle. I was running around getting three of my brothers ready for school and the other two ready to go back to bed. I didn't have time to eat, but I poured myself a cup of coffee with my five teaspoons of sugar. (I can never get enough sugar.) When I picked up the cup—how it happened, I don't know —but the bottom fell out, and all the hot coffee fell in my lap. Aside from the burn, I was devastated because this was all I had to wear. I got down on my knees and prayed to God for a miracle. Then I took out the ironing board, plugged in the iron, and when it was hot enough I ironed my skirt inside out. It was wool, so I had to be careful. A miracle! I saw a miracle! The stain somehow pulled through to the inside of the skirt and didn't show on the outside. If God can make a stain disappear, why can't he obliterate "Uncle" Jack. The janitors erase obscene things written on the walls in school. Why doesn't God erase *him*? I would applaud with the erasers. CLAP!... CLAP!... CLAP!... C C C, L L L, A A A, P P P.

A thesaurus? What a treasure! There's nothing stopping me now. Words, words, and more words! I was right on target with the word "treasure." Look at this, the dictionary says the word itself comes from the Greek "Thesaurus." Treasure, a treasury of words and information. A book of synonyms. This is truly something to cherish. HER vocabulary never seems to expand. Maybe I should give her a Thesaurus. No, that would be a travesty to see something precious torn to shreds.

I think my music teacher is going to be my favorite. They're all very nice, but Mr. Parisi is *the* one! I was trembling when he asked me to come up to the piano and sing by myself. His whole self smiles while he's conducting us. I felt kind of badly when he told me that sophomores can't join the chorus. My brother Robert is in it, but he's a senior. I wish I could sing in the chorus with him. Maybe he'd be friendlier.

"Claudette, I've decided to make an exception. I want you in the chorus."

"Me?"

"Yes, you."

"Oh thank you, Mr. Parisi." This is too thrilling. I'd rather sing than eat. That girl who plays the piano is excellent. I'd love to play like that, but I'll settle for listening to her.

I think our Spanish teacher likes Tony. He's the only one who she doesn't get mad at when he doesn't have his homework done. He's tall and kind of handsome. I think he's already eighteen. He's older than most of us. He flirts with her outrageously, and she gets all red and giggles. He scares me when he loses his temper, though. Some of the kids say he has a sickness. I wonder what it is?

"Is it true that you're a milkman and deliver milk before school?"

"That's right. Would you like to go out on my route with me some morning?"

"I'd love it. What time?"... "Four o'clock tomorrow morning?"

"I'll pick you up."

If I ask HER, she'll never let me go. I'll just go and come back before anyone wakes up. This is an adventure. It's so dark out here. Here he comes. No wonder he's always falling asleep in school if he has to get up this early every day.

"How do you remember how many quarts each person gets?"

"I have a list, and after a while, I memorize it."

"Tony, you don't look happy in school. You scare me sometimes when you lose your temper."

"It's my sickness. I'm going to die soon."

"Why are you saying such a thing? You're young; you're not going to die. Besides I'm just getting to know you, and I like you a lot. So you can't die."

"You'll see."

Why does he talk like that?

"Thanks for taking me. See you in school."

"Thanks for going with me. I really liked talking with you. Mostly, everybody is afraid of me."

"Tony won't be in class with us anymore. He died this morning in an accident. He had been suffering with a brain tumor and had a seizure and crashed into a tree when he was working on this milk route earlier today."

Oh, no! No wonder he was always sad or angry. He really knew that he was going to die. Oh God, I need more answers because this certainly brings up more questions.

"Tony, I'm glad I wasn't afraid of you. I knew you were hurting, but I didn't know why. Maybe I'll see you again some day, somewhere."

"You want me to sing a solo?"

"It's just a small part in *The Night Before Christmas*, but I don't want you to tell anybody until we do it in rehearsal with the chorus."

"Yes, sir."

I dread going to Health class today. We're going to be practicing bandaging each other's arms, legs, and ankles. What will I do if I have to take my shoes off? My feet and my shoes smell so terrible.

"All right, girls. You all have a partner. Take off your

shoes and take turns wrapping each other's ankle as you learned to do if it had been sprained."

"I'll do yours first, Claudette; then you can do mine."

Oh no! "Okay, here's my foot."

"Excuse me a minute, Claudette."

What's she going to see the teacher for? As if I didn't know. I can't stand the odor myself. I was hoping for a miracle.

"Claudette, Marion is going to practice on one of the other girls, and I'm going to demonstrate on you."

"Yes, Ma'am." Is there a hole I can crawl into?

My box of treasures is really growing in the attic. I love to come up and look at them. Look at all of the grammar notebooks and math books and paintings and concert programs. I can't wait to read my report cards to my children and show them daddy's signature."Who's that on the stairs?"

"Where's my mother?"... "What are *you* doing here now?"

"I didn't pick her up yet. Don't move, and shut your mouth."

"The kids are going to wake up. Get away from me. Stop it! Stop it! Don't spit on me like that. You're hurting me."

"Shut your mouth, B—, and don't move."

"Claudette! Claudette, what are you doing up there? I heard a lot of noise."

My sweat is sweating. "I just dropped some things, Leon. Get back into bed. Here I come."

"You, pig! I'll tell."

"You, whore. Nobody will believe you."

He's right except for the part about being a whore. WHORE... WHORE... WHORE... W W W, H H H, O O O, R R R, E E E. "Here's a drink of water, Leon. Now go to sleep."

"Good night, Mommy."

"You're silly. Good night."

Today is Friday? What happened to Tuesday, Wednesday, and Thursday? I can't for the life of me remember. How can I be functioning and producing when I'm not even aware that I'm existing? My hives are as big as quarters. I hate it when they cover my whole nose. I look like a clown.

Who is he? He's too cute for words. I wonder why he's in the principal's office?

"May I help you, Claudette?"

"Yes, please. Mr. Parisi asked me to bring this note to you."

"Thank you."

"You're welcome."... "Hi, I'm Claudette. What's your name?"

"Arthur."

"Are you in trouble?"

"I usually am."

"I've never seen you before."

"You will. I'm new in this school."

"I hope everything is okay. See you around." My heart is pounding like a jackhammer. He looked so adorable in his navy turtleneck sweater and his naturally curly hair. I sure hope Arthur shows up in my classes. I'm in love!

"Hi, Claudette. This is for you."

"A poem for me? Arthur, this is so sweet!" A poet, besides being adorable!

"Would it be all right if I called you?"

"Oh please, that would be great. Only call at eight o'clock though." I'll have the five of them in bed by then, and SHE and HE will be gone. He loves music and poetry. Even my eyelids are trembling! Why are my palms sweating when I'm only speaking on the phone? "The movies?"... "I'll have to ask my mother."... "Sunday? I'll let you know."

"Hi, Claudette, this is Arthur. Can you go on Sunday?"

"I can go, but I have to bring four of my little brothers with me."

"Yes, I can meet you at the park, but I have to bring four of my brothers with me."

"Yes, I can come to the schoolyard to play baseball, but I have to bring four of my brothers with me."

"Can't you go anywhere without bringing your brothers?"

"It's my responsibility to take care of them. If I don't bring them wherever I want to go, then I can't go."

"Claudette, this is Arthur. Would you do me a favor? I'd like you to call my older sister."

"For what?"

"She'll tell you."

"Okay, what's her name?"

"Arthur wants you to know, Claudette, that he really, really likes you, but he didn't have the nerve to tell you something. So he asked me to do it. He thought maybe I could help you."

"Help me with what?"

"Well... You have bad odors. Maybe you need to go to the dentist; and you should ask your mother about a deodorant."

"What's a deodorant?"

"After you wash under your arms, it's a cream that you rub in so that you don't smell bad. When a young girl starts to get her period usually she starts to get an unpleasant odor under her arms. Boys do, too."

"What's your period? Do boys get it, too?"

"Claudette, if you have some time now, there are some things I'm going to explain to you."

"If you're going to talk about the dentist, we can't afford to have me go. I wanted to, but my mother said we didn't have the money."

"Go to the school nurse and talk to her. I know there's an arrangement where they help people who can't afford medical or dental care. Now listen to me carefully; there are other things that I want to explain to you now..."

"Do you think that my older brothers know the things that you just talked to me about?"

"Probably."

"Do you think the other girls in my class know?"

"Probably."

"I feel so stupid."

"You're not stupid, Claudette. Young people just need to be taught certain things, and no one taught you. You'll probably hear some of these things in your Health class."

"I'm terribly embarrassed, Gloria, but thank you. Can I ask you a question? I heard what you said about how a girl gets pregnant, but is there another way?"

"What other way?"

"Well, if a boy pees on a girl, can that make her pregnant?"

"No, Claudette. There's only one way to get pregnant…"

Oh God, please don't let me be pregnant!! Don't cry. Don't cry.

"Don't you love the movies, Claudette?"

"Yes, Leon. Now you and the boys be quiet."

"Hey look, Claudette, there's Arthur."

"I see him."

"He's with Sheila."

"I see her. Be quiet and watch the movie." I bet Sheila isn't sitting there with pieces of cloth stuffed into her armpits so that she doesn't smell. I'm sure she has deodorant. When I get a job and get some money, I'm going to buy deodorant. I'll ask Gloria where to get it. As long as I wash these pieces of cloth every night and don't move too much or raise my arms, I'll be all right. I'll just raise my hand with my elbow on the desk. I'm so, so tired.

"Here, *you* get on my back. I'll carry you, and the rest of you stay by my side. Philip, just keep the cloth pressed against your eye."

"But I'm bleeding."

"I know, but just try to keep the cloth over your eye; press it hard so it will help the bleeding to stop. Dr. Strictor will take care of it when we get there. Leon, Matthew, Daniel, just hang on to me and don't let go when we cross the streets. We all have to hurry."

"Is the doctor here, Mrs. Strictor? Philip got hit with a

baseball bat, and his head is split open above his eye. I had to bring all the kids because there was no one home. Go with Dr. Strictor, Philip. He'll help you."

"Come on, little fella; we'll stitch that right up for you. I won't hurt you too much. It will pinch just a little."

"Let me drive you all home, Claudette."

"I'd appreciate it, but SHE's going to be furious."

"Things aren't any better? Well, just do the best you can. Before you know it, you'll be out on your own, doing what you want. You're going to make a wonderful teacher, Claudette."

"I hope so." If I live long enough!

Thank God SHE's not home yet. Let me relax from cleaning all the blood before the screaming starts. It seems to me that all that raging would wear HER out. I guess that's why SHE never gets up in the morning.

"What is wrong with me, doctor? Blood is just gushing out of me in big chunks. I'm running out of newspaper to soak it up."

"I've told your mother that you have to get more rest. You can't be picking the children up and carrying them all the time. You're a very fragile little girl. I'm going to give you some medication to stop the bleeding. It should slow down in a couple of days."

"How am I going to take care of the boys and go to school?"

"You're not; you're going to stay in this bed for at least a week. I'll talk to your mother."

"Claudette, Uncle Jack is taking me to the Bingo. Robert will be home. You can help him with the dishes."

"Yes, Ma'am."

"What's the matter with you?"

I'm not going to answer him.

"Uncle Jack asked you a question. Answer him! Never mind. The dramatic one is pulling an act like her old man. She's just a dramatic little b—."

"Let's go."

"Robert! Robert! Bring me a towel and some more newspaper quick!" What day is it? Thursday? Friday? FRIDAY... FRIDAY... FRIDAY... F F F, R R R, I I I, D D D, A A A, Y Y Y. Please just let me sleep.

19

A Time To Keep

"This is Jackie; she'll be playing the piano for us."

"Hi there. You have a really nice voice."

"Hi, you play the piano beautifully."

"Thanks. Anytime you'd like to practice, I'll play for you."

"That would be great. How about if we meet in the music room at lunchtime?"

"See you there."

I could just listen to her play the piano for eternity. I hope that we stay friends for that long, too. She doesn't have any brothers or sisters. I wonder what that's like, with no line of people standing outside the bathroom door? From what she says, her parents are very strict. That's okay as long as they don't beat her. I hope they don't.

Every single morning, first period, (Whoops. there's that word. Does everybody hear it the way I do?) we have chorus. Some people don't like to sing in the morning. I could sing morning, noon, and night and still not have enough. I wonder when he's going to let the rest of the chorus hear my solo?

"Good morning."

"Good morning, Mr. Parisi."

"This morning we're going to start working on *The Night Before Christmas*. Our concert will be here before you know it."

Today's the day, Claudette. Hold your knees together so that they don't knock, or at least keep them in time with the music. Everyone in the whole world should be able to sing in a chorus. It's an extraordinary experience. I can just feel everyone's voice sinking into my pores and flooding my heart. There isn't a dictionary comprehensive enough or a thesaurus complete enough to describe the joy of music, so I won't try. Music just is!

Get ready, Claudette. Here comes your part. He's pointing at you. Sing! *He spoke not a word but went straight to his work. He filled all the stockings and turned with a jerk. And laying a finger aside of his nose, and giving a nod, up the chimney he rose.*

Everybody is staring at me.

"Did you ever hear anything so beautiful?"

Mr. Parisi is talking about me. I'll remember this moment forever.

"Claudette, do you want to stop at the chocolate shop on the way home?"

"Sure, Jackie, but I can't stay too long; I have to get home." It's good that I saved a quarter and didn't eat lunch. I was hoping she'd ask me to go with her. I think she really cares for me. She's my first real grown-up friend. I wonder whatever happened to Louise? After they moved, I never heard from her again.

I feel so adult going to the chocolate shop. Jackie always sits on the side facing the door. I sit on the other side, and we both stretch one leg out on the seat. Now that we're comfortable, we discuss life. I don't think Jackie is too happy at home. It's nothing that she says, it's her eyes. A lot of times her mouth is smiling, but her eyes aren't. I'm convinced that there can't possibly be anyone in the whole world that plays the piano as beautifully as Jackie. She plays a piece for me that's completely enthralling, *The Rustle Of Spring*. I'm sure she's sick of me asking her to play it, but if I asked her to play it a hundred times in a row, she would. That's the kind of person she is.

Oh God, what would I do without her? It's going to be terrible when she graduates and goes to the conservatory in Boston. Hopefully, by some miracle, I'll be there with her the following year. I know I'm lingering here too long, but I don't want to leave Jackie and go home. To say SHE'll be annoyed if I get home late would be an understatement. How about furious, Claudette? Enraged? Infuriated? Rabid? Raging? Ranting? Raving? Thank you, *Roget's Thesaurus*, without you I'd be vocabulary poor and speechless.

"I have to run, Jackie. See you tomorrow." Run, Claudette, run! SHE's going to kill me! Well, it's almost worth it. That cocoa and whipped cream was delicious. Thank you, God, I've found a soul mate. We're kindred spirits.

"You g—d-d—mned son-of-a-b—, what did I tell you about being late? When you finish cleaning the sh—t off of the crib and the wall, get down here and get to the store. AND GET THOSE DIAPERS OFF OF THE STAIRS AND CLEANED OUT! DO YOU HEAR ME?"

"Yes, Ma'am." I can't believe SHE really wonders if I can hear HER. I'm curious as to what SHE'd do if I said "no." Don't even joke about that, Claudette. SHE'll accompany HER words with the strap. I can live without that orchestration. Just clean the feces and get to the store. Save your legs. You don't need any blood drawn today.

"Claudette, do you want to stop at the music store on the way home after school?"

"If we hurry." Now this is another place where I would

love to live. Mr. Z is very patient with us. He lets us go into the little booths and play our favorite records. Mine are always Jane Powell. I know every song she's ever sung. I wish we had a record player; however, at least I can stop here and listen. We're in an extra hurry today, so Jackie and I will do a quick song.

"Okay, Jackie. How about *Love Is Where You Find It?* Introduction, please..."

Now that song took a lot of energy from both of us.
"Let's go."
"Wait! What's your name? Who are you?"
"I'm Claudette."
"Claudette, you have such a gift. I want to train you. You must go to Julliard in New York City with me. I must speak to your parents."

"Do you believe this, Jackie? He wants me to go to Julliard. Wouldn't that be miraculous? He's going to speak to my parents. This is unbelievable!"
"Let me know what happens."
"I'll call you." I forgot about the filth. He'll turn around and leave when he sees it. Why did I give him my address?

"Madam, you must let me train your daughter's voice. She has such a gift. We will pay all of her expenses. It won't cost you a dime. She must be given this opportunity."

"She has responsibilities here. She's not going anywhere."

"Please, Madam. I'm imploring you. You must give her this chance."

"I said she's not going anywhere. She has work to do here."

No Julliard? No bright Broadway? Okay! I'll sing upstairs day after day.

"Please, if you reconsider, you can reach me at this number."

At this NUMBER... NUMBER... NUMBER... N N N, U U U, M M M, B B B, E E E, R R R. I wonder if I'll ever cry. I wish right now that I would die. SIGH... MY... PIE... FLY... STY... DRY... PLY... FRY...

"You can take the job for the summer as long as you're home to get the boys up. You be back here no later than nine o'clock."

If I leave here at five o'clock, I'll get there by six o'clock. I'll work two hours preparing the trays for the patients, then I'll leave there at eight o'clock and I'll be back by nine o'clock. Finally, my own bra and some deodorant!

"Guess what, Jackie? I have a summer job." As glad as I am though, I'll be happy to get back to school and chorus and my adventures with Jackie. Wait! Also Katz musicals and the chocolate shop.

The whole town looks like it's asleep. I guess there aren't that many people awake at five o'clock in the morning. Look at that huge building going up. It looks like a big shell or amphitheater. I think "amphitheater" is the correct word. I'll check it when I get home. I bet with its being empty like that, the acoustics are remarkable. Should I? There's no one around. Why not?

Love is where you'll find it...

What an incredible sound. I'm going to stop here every morning. This will be my song-stop: *Presenting Claudette!*

Wait till I tell Jackie about this. I have my own theater and stage. I bet the man from Julliard would like to come and see me perform, except maybe not at five o'clock in the morning. "But, Madam, she has such a gift." GIFT... GIFT... GIFT... G G G, I I I, F F F, T T T.

Back to school. I couldn't be happier away from the bowels of Hell. My English teacher said that she went to see *South Pacific* on Broadway last weekend. She said I really must go. I'll be lucky if I get to see South Main Street.

SHE is so furious with me. I understand that someone from the school contacted her to see if she would agree to place me with another family. I can't believe that they did that. If SHE was violent before, no one can imagine what it's like now!

These boys are draining the life out of me. I see filthy diapers in my sleep. I'm afraid to close my eyes because of the horrific nightmares that I have. Gray Chrysler, PH 700—Jack is excruciatingly vile. I'm just so tired.

"No, Claudette, it's not Tuesday; it's Friday. Where's your mind today? In the clouds?"

"No, sir, I guess I just forgot. I get confused a lot. I don't know why."

"Well, don't get confused about this. You're going to sing *Oh, Holy Night.*"

"Jackie, Jackie, I'm going to sing *Oh, Holy Night* in the Christmas concert. We'll have to practice a lot."

"That's great, Claudette. That's just great."

"But he said the girls all have to wear dresses, not skirts and blouses."

"Too bad. You have what you have."

"My yellow sweater and my gray skirt?" Don't cry, Claudette, or you'll be wearing a black eye, too. SHE might even split your lip, and you already have a big ringworm on your chin and your top lip. Maybe my sister will give me something.

"Naomi, do you have anything I can wear to the Christmas concert? I'm going to sing a solo. All the girls are suppose to wear dresses."

"I'll bring you something."

Where is she? I have to be there in an hour and a half?

A black suit? It looks like it belongs to a businessman.
"It's a beautiful suit. I wore it on my honeymoon."
Right! Ten years ago! Good grief, look at the shoes she brought, with those ankle straps and big thick tall heels. I'll trip and kill myself. "I can't wear these shoes with socks." SHE's getting madder by the minute.
"Well, we're not going to go out and buy you any stockings."
Horror of horrors! SHE's pulling off her girdle and stockings.
"Put these on. They're good enough."

Here I stand, "Pagliacci" on the stage, in front of all the students and their families and the teachers, in my sister's black, man-tailored suit, shoes that don't fit, smelly girdle and stockings, and a big ringworm on my chin and over my lip. Someone has vacuumed my tear ducts.
Jackie's playing the introduction. I'm so glad I have you for my friend, Jackie.
Oh Holy Night. The stars are brightly shining. It is the night of our dear Saviour's birth...
A standing ovation? Encore? Encore? Look at Mr. Parisi beam! I love you, Mr. Parisi. I love you, Jackie.

20

A Time To Implode

"He has what?"

"Shut up, Claudette. SHE'll hear us. Whisper!"

"They took Uncle Jack to the hospital."

"He's not our uncle."

"I know that."

"What's wrong with him?"

"He has cancer and TB."

"What's TB?"

"It's when you have something wrong with your lungs."

"Oh, Robert, is he going to die?"

"I don't know. I just heard mother say that we all have to go to the doctor and have a TB test, because he was always around us."

Oh my God, especially me! I don't dare tell Robert. Am I going to die?

"When do we have to go?"
"Tomorrow."
"I hope it doesn't hurt."

"All of you have to come back in a week, and we'll see if any of you had a positive reaction."
"What if we do?"
"We'll talk about it then."

The stress is agonizing. I won't sleep for a week. At least things are quieter around here. SHE just calls a cab to go to Bingo and to the hospital.

What a relief! All of us are negative. Now what? Nobody asks HER anything, and SHE doesn't volunteer anything. SHE says I should go and see him. My brother's friend Harry, who lives next door, says he'll take me. He's nice enough. He's always looking at me like Jack does, though. It makes me uncomfortable.

This is shocking! He looks like a skeleton. If his name weren't on the chart at the end of the bed, I wouldn't have known who he was. The nurse says that he doesn't know that we're here.

Well, I went, just like SHE told me to. I hate remembering him like that.

"You boys stop fooling around and to to sleep. I'm exhausted. I want to go to sleep myself."
"Good night, Claudette."
"Good night, boys."

"Who's shaking me? What's wrong ?"
"Get up, B—, and get your clothes on. They just called and said that Jack is dying. You're going to the hospital with me. Hurry up; the cab will be here."

Good grief! It's two o'clock in the morning. Why is SHE taking *me*?

"Come in this room with me, you little lying b—. You wanted him dead. Now you're going to watch him die."
I'm going to watch him die? Please, God, deliver me from this horror.
"Get back and let the priest give him the last rites. Get over here, you little wh—re, and watch him. This is what you wanted, right?"

I'm struck dumb. This isn't happening. What is the nurse thinking? It's four o'clock in the morning. How long do I have to stand here?

"Doctor."

"Yes, Nurse?"

"His vital signs are improving. Maybe he'll hang on a little longer."

"You and your daughter might as well go home. We'll call you if there's any change."

I might as well stay up because I have to go to school, and it's almost time to get the kids up. I'm so tired.

Thank God I got through the day.

"Come on, boys, I was up very late last night. Please let's all go to sleep."

"What? What?"

"Get up, Wh—re. The hospital just called. He's not going to last much longer, and you're going to watch him die. That should make you happy. The cab is on its way."

My bones and my brain are disconnected. What kind of torture is this?

"Stand right here, you little sl—t, and watch him. You'll hear the rattle when he dies. This is what you wanted, so here you are!"

"Doctor, his vital signs are improving again. He's rallying."

"He certainly is."

"Well, you might as well go back home. We'll call you if there's any change."

My whole self is paralyzed.

It's six o'clock, so I might as well stay up. I have to get the kids up, fed, and ready for school pretty soon anyway. At least I was able to see the sunrise; that was beautiful. How am I ever going to get through a day in school? I don't even know what I'm saying half of the time.

"Claudette, are you all right?"

"Yes, Mr. Parisi." Who would believe this drama? *I* can't believe it even though it's happening to me!

"Get dressed, B—. The hospital just called, and the cab is on its way."

"Again?"

This just has to be a very bad dream.

"Get in the room. Get by the bed. Listen! Hear the rattle? That's the death rattle. You happy? This should make you happy! Hear it? He's dead. You're not leaving this room until they pull the sheet up over his face. Happy, B—?"

"Daddy! Daddy! Please do something!"

"Don't upset your mother. Just keep her happy."

Dear, God, may I please have a rattle?

21

A Time To Throw Stones

SHE's going out with whom? The garbage man? Get me out of here! Get me out of here! Jackie, I miss you so much. It's not the same in school without you. One more year to go.

"No, we don't have any money for you to get a yearbook. No, we don't have any money for you to get a class ring."

"Class, I'd like to introduce you to Angelique. She's from Greece. She'll be in this class, so you can all help her with her English."

She certainly is pretty. This must be scary for her.

"Would you like to sit here?"
"Thank you."

"Good morning, Claudette."
"Good morning, Mr. Parisi. I'm really looking forward to our music theory class. There's so much to learn. This is Angelique. She's from Greece, and she'll be in all of our classes. I'm going to try to help her with English."

"Angelique, are you all right? You always seem so sad."
"I just want to go to school."
"You're in school, so what's the problem?"
"Never mind."

"Miss Foster, Angelique hasn't been in school for a week. Do you know if she's all right?"
"Angelique won't be coming back to school. She's getting married."
"Married?"
"Actually, that's why she was brought to this country. She was supposed to be given in marriage to someone that her parents arranged it with. That's their custom. When she got here, she didn't want to marry him, and apparently her parents let her come to school. I understand the man got very upset and said that she would have to marry him because her parents had already agreed to it. It seems that he had already given them some money."
"That's terrible! She had to marry him? That's sad. No

wonder she looked so unhappy."

"Sometimes people have to do what they have to do, Claudette, even if it's difficult."

Hmmm... If she only knew!

She's getting married; she's getting married? That's it! I'll get married! Harry's always talking about getting married. If I get married, I can get out of the house. No, the law says that I have to stay there until I'm twenty-one. SHE would never sign for me. It's worth a try, though.

"Harry, what do you think about getting married?"
"Sure."

"I'm going to ask my mother. I know SHE won't say 'yes,' but it's nice to dream about living my own life."

"Harry and I want to get married."
"Fine. You'll bring your books back and notify the school that you're leaving."

"Fine? She said, 'fine'?" I can't believe it. I don't want to get married; I just want to get out of here. I want to graduate, and I want to go to college and be a teacher. "I don't really want to get married. I just said that."

"Look, B—, you said you want to get married, so you're getting married. As a matter of fact, I'm going to the school with you and make sure that you bring your books back. Harry, you'll drive us there."

"Please, you can't let her leave school. She just has a few months till graduation. In that she's an honor student, she's going to receive scholarships to go to college. We have wonderful plans for her."

"You take care of your school, and I'll take care of my daughter. Give them your books!!"

"Yes, Ma'am."

"Mr. Parisi, this is my mother."

"How do you do? What's this I hear, Claudette, that you're leaving school? You can't! I need you in the chorus. I've already picked out your solos for our concert. You have to go on with your music."

He has tears in his eyes.

"I'll decide what she's going to do. Let's get out of here!"

My books! My books! My dear precious treasures! I'm so sorry; I apologize for leaving you here. At least, I'm leaving my fingerprints with you.

"Go to church and tell the priest that you want to be married in two weeks."

"I can't; Harry isn't Catholic."

"Then find another church "

"Yes, Ma am."

"You'll wear your sister's wedding gown."

"A party for me?"

"Yes, some of the kids from school are going to have a

party for you."

Is it true that some of the kids are drinking alcohol?
I wouldn't do that because I made a vow in church that I
wouldn't drink until I'm twenty-one.

"Here's some punch, Claudette."
"Thanks." This is delicious. Fill it up again! Again!
What's wrong with my head. I feel *very* dizzy. What are
they saying? Someone spiked my punch. What's that? I
can't stand up. Is that my voice I hear screaming? "I don't
want to get married! I don't want to get married! I want to
go to school."
Is that Dr. Strictor standing over me?
"That's all right, Claudette. That's all right. You don't
have to get married. I'll talk to your mother. Just get her
home, Harry. She'll be better tomorrow."
"No! No! I can't go home. I can't go back there. Can I go
to your house, Jackie? I feel so sick."
"Sure."

I don't think Jackie's mother is too happy about this,
but what am I going to do? It's two o'clock in the morning.
I have to go somewhere. Who's at the door at this hour?
My brother Robert? He came all the way from down south
for the wedding? Sorry, Robert.

"Mother says you better get home, or she's coming after

you herself."

I certainly can't subject this family to one of her scenes. Okay, here I come."

"You're drunk, you b—."

"I don't want to get married. I just don't want to get married. I want to go to school."

"You g—d-d—mned son-of-a-b—, you're going to get married if I have to drag you down the aisle!"

Look at this. They're dressing me up like a doll. Nothing is real. I feel like I'm floating. Who is this person dressed in a robe asking me if I take this man to be my husband? How did I get here? *Where* am I? Are those tears coming out of my eyes? It can't be; I don't cry. The man in the robe is giving me a handkerchief. No, I'm not going to say I want this man for my husband. Dr. Strictor said I don't have to get married. Did he forget to talk to my mother? I wish my sister would stop poking me with her elbow. She keeps saying, You *have* to say it! You *have* to say it! No, I don't!!!!!

What am I doing back in my mother's house? Harry and I *live* here? We went to New York for the weekend on a honeymoon? We're going to be living here with my mother, and I'm still going to be taking care of the children? We're going to be sleeping in the living room? This has to be some kind of a cruel joke, or else I'm dreaming. Why can't I remember what happened? I just remember my sister telling me that I had to say it!

"Claudette, get upstairs and get the baby up."

"Harry, what are we doing here?"

"Your mother said it would be cheaper for us to stay here. Don't get her mad; she's helping us."

THERE ARE NO MORE WORDS!!!

I don't know where I'm going, but I'm going. Dad will be leaving in a couple of minutes. I can't believe SHE even goes to Bingo on Sunday.

"Harry, you must be tired after that big meal. Why don't you go up and lie down on one of the boys beds and take a nap.

"Okay, Claudette."

"Goodbye, Daddy, I love you." Sometimes I think I should be angry with you for not helping me, but then I understand you. You can't even help yourself. (One day I would hold Daddy in my arms as he died. It was only fair that I should have been the one to be with him, just the two of us, at that moment in time.)

"Loretta, may I stay with you and your mom for a few days? I don't want anyone to know where I am. I have to get myself together."... "Where's my suitcase? This paper bag holds everything I own."... "I'll start at the beginning so you can understand why I'm here..."

"So now I have to make a decision. I will *not* go back there. I can't! I know a couple, a husband and wife, who live in Coventry. They're dance instructors. I met them when they came to school to help us with a show we put on. I'm going to call them and see if they'll help me to get a job and find a place to live."

"They said, 'yes,' and that they'll pick me up tomorrow evening. Thank you so much for helping me, and *please* don't tell anyone that you saw me."

"If we didn't have just two rooms, you could stay here permanently. I'm sure we'll find something in the paper. Look at this. Howard Johnson's need a waitress. Do you think you could do that?"

"I'll do anything. Will you take me there for an interview?"

"I've got it! The job is mine! Now let's find a room FOR ME."

"I'm Mrs. Hart, and this is my husband, Mr. Hart. The rent will be three dollars a week, and you'll have your own bathroom. I'll give you clean sheets and towels once a week. Also, you can use the kitchen if you want to make tea or something."

My own bedroom? My own bathroom? No mucus mountain? Clean sheets and towels? Could there be anything else in life that could make me this happy?

"Who's knocking on my door?"

"It's Mrs. Hart. You've been sleeping for almost twenty hours. I just came to check on you. Your friends called several times, but I told them I didn't want to disturb you. You seemed so tired, and you looked so pale. Can I make you some tea?"

"Thank you very, very much. I have to get myself ready to start my new job tomorrow."

So this is what freedom is. I wish I was back in school, but I can't think about that. Everybody at work calls me "Mrs. Clean." Now that's a name I don't mind. I can't get over how fast the months are flying. I hope my interview at the radio station goes well tomorrow. It was nice of my customer to tell me about it. Imagine me, reading stories to children on the Children's Hour? I love to read. Who knows, maybe the job can turn into something even better. It's a start. "May I help you, sir? Can I get you some coffee?"

"Is your name, Claudette?"

"Yes, it is."

"Mine is Browning. I'm a private detective. You have some explaining to do. I've already contacted your husband. He's on his way here now."

God help me, I'm going to vomit! "Excuse, me, I'll be back."

"You have to stay with me. We're married."

"I don't want to be married."

"It's too late for that. You have responsibilities."

I loathe that WORD; I abhor it. "I'll run away again."

"I'll find you."

"Why do you even want me?"

"You know why."

"Go get another girl."

"I already have you. I always told myself that one day I would reform a whore. Let's go!"

"I'm what? I can't be! I'm going to have a what?"

"Yes, Claudette, you're pregnant. You're going to have a baby."

I can't! I'm only seventeen. I'm a baby. It can't be true, Doctor!

"It's true, Claudette. These things happen."

HAPPEN... HAPPEN... HAPPEN... H H H, A A A, P P P, P P P, E E E, N N N.

"Naomi, I'm pregnant."

"So what do you expect if you're married?"

"You know, Naomi, I'll never understand why SHE went along with my getting married. I was sure SHE'd say no, but it's like SHE couldn't marry me off fast enough."

"She thought you were pregnant."

"She thought I was pregnant?!" SHE *THOUGHT* I WAS PREGNANT? I WENT THROUGH ALL OF THIS BECAUSE SHE *THOUGHT* I WAS PREGNANT? AND NOBODY ASKED ME?

"Too late now. Stop fussing."

My brain absolutely cannot digest this information. Don't think, Claudette.

"Now that we have our own apartment, I'm going to go over to the house and get all of my treasures from the attic that I have saved—my notebooks, my paintings, and all my precious things. Well, they're precious to me."

"She threw them all away."

"SHE what?"

"She took everything in the attic and threw it all out."

I am a cave of despair. I feel acrimony seeping out of my marrow. Contain it, Claudette. Just perhaps, at some point in time, someone told her, "You better not cry."

22

A Time To Uproot What Was Planted

Here we are, little baby in my belly. Just you and I, about to begin a daunting adventure. I'm very scared. I know what I *want* to do for you. I'm just afraid that I don't know *how* to do it. There were so many things in my life that I didn't know how to do. That deficiency definitely compounded my problems. There are so many things in my life that I *still* don't know how to do. Maybe we can learn together.

(Just before my mom died, I was alone with her, and I asked her "Why? Why did you act towards me, like you did?" SHE simply said, "I never liked you." Although I don't understand how you can dislike someone you don't even know, I did appreciate her candor. I guess everybody doesn't like everybody.)

I'm going to try to know everything about you. Most importantly, I want you to like yourself.

As you grow, you'll probably think that you really know me, but decades later you might find that it wasn't always the way it seemed. I'm sure that the same will be true about me thinking I know you. Perhaps we'll laugh or maybe cry someday when we say, "Is that what you thought? Is that what you felt?... How funny!... How sad!" I'm glad you don't know how afraid I am. Maybe you wouldn't want to come out.

I feel that I should have something special to give to you, but I don't. I can give you a clean house and a lovely room, where you won't be ashamed to bring your friends. Maybe if I make it too clean, you'll write a book about me someday. "She was so clean, she drove us all crazy."

I will give you my time and my attention. I won't use profanity. I'll let beautiful music fill your ears. I can give you a love and appreciation for the beauty and the marvels of creation. I'll introduce you to your Creator, but you'll have to choose to cultivate your own relationship with him. I can teach you to care for older people and make them feel cherished. I'll teach you the value of appropriate grammar and good manners. These two treasures can open many doors for you. I'll expose you to breathtaking art and the thrill of music that will stir your soul.

I offer you these gifts: love, sympathy, empathy for others, and a passion for truth, fairness and justice. I'll also let you cry.

Maybe these gifts won't be gifts to you at all. Perhaps in some instances they'll prove to be a burden, an intrusion into your own personality or conscience. Possibly we all just have to develop our own gifts.

I guess that all I can really give to you is the gift of life.

Oh no, you're beginning to make your entrance. I'm not ready; you're mother is mentally and emotionally cracked and splintered. Yet, I have to meet this challenge...

Claudette, you darn well better cry!

23

A Time To Bring Stones Together

"Claudette, here's your beautiful little baby girl. Take her, but make sure you cradle her head."

"I know how to do it." Look at her little fingers. And look at her tiny toes. And how pink she is. Oh my goodness, what am I doing? She's hungry. Let me feed her..."

Well I'm certainly not on Broadway right now, am I? But I guess a hospital bed can be a stage if you imagine it to be. And I guess Julliard will eventually get along without me. There's no reason why I only have to sing opera. There's certainly other songs to be sung. And there's poems to be written and pictures to be painted.

Just because my life has taken a detour, doesn't mean my dreams have too. I'll just blossom where I'm planted.

"Tell me how you like this tune, my little Robin. You may hum along if you please. Here we go, *Somewhere over the rainbow...*"

Placergold

I was born in New England on August 25th, 1933. My formal education spanned Kindergarten to my senior year in high school. I didn't get a class ring. First, because I couldn't afford one, and second, because I left school before the year was over.

My appearance? People refer to me as "The lady with the fuzzy red hair and all the purple rings." (At least they call me a lady!)

At the insistence of my youngest daughter, I earned my GED in 1998 at the age of sixty-five. I've never qualified for letters after my name from any institution, so, I made up my own. C for cleaning person, P for poetry writer, S for singer, D for drawing, M for mother, another D for decorator, V for Vitamin store owner, T for thinker, F for friend, and W for whatever.

That's who I am, Janet Barré, C.P.S.D.M.D.V.T.F.W.

I began my family at age 18, a child having a child. Enough said. After much searching, I found a faith that satisfied my spiritual curiosity. Along with caring for my home and children, the ministry became an integral part of my life.

In my thirties, I came to understand that hypoglycemia was at the root of my health problems, (which I will address in my forthcoming book, *Look At Me, You Might See You*). I became involved in the health food industry and now own and operate a health food store in Newington, Connecticut.

In my sixties, again my youngest daughter nagged me... this time to write a book. She would say, "You love to write; why don't you write a book?" Looking back over the traumatic events of my life I knew that I had something to say. Although it certainly incorporates these issues, this book is not just an exposé or a story of survival. I had an extended agenda: to increase society's awareness of the connection between sugar, alcohol, and drug abuse and the resulting mental, physical, and emotional devastation.

For the past thirty-five years, I have been involved in intensive research concerning the application of nutritional solutions to the aforementioned problems. The recollections of my childhood coupled with my acquired knowledge, has intensified my focus.

Do I believe that there was more amiss with my family than the abuse of sugar and alcohol? Of course. However, I have learned from personal experience and in my dealings with others that these substances definitely produce a chemical imbalance that exacerbates already existing problems. WE ARE WHAT WE EAT!

My evidence is further supported by the thousands of people whom I have personally helped over the years by sharing this information. I am not a doctor. I'm not recommending medical treatment. I'm offering a view of my life and how I dealt with it. More than that, I passionately encourage people to look at me... I can't help but wonder if the lives of my family and myself would have been favorably altered if we had been aware of the connection between sugar and alcohol abuse and the resulting, otherwise unexplainable, exhaustion, violence, depression, and sundry symptoms.

I'm convinced that it would have, which is why I've been educating people for decades on this issue and will continue to do so in the future. Choice books and verbal communication are a lifeline to be treasured.

Looking back on our lives is like watching a video that we've seen many times before. Hopefully, each time we view it, we learn something new. I have. I'm inviting you to relive this journey with me. Hopefully we'll both benefit from the trip. Thank you for your company.

BOARD OF EDUCATION

MERIDEN, CONN.

TERM REPORT
OF

Janet Baire

Grade ....VI....   ....B. Franklin.... ......School

19..44-45

Signature of Parent

Health

We are sorry Janet lost time due to illness. We miss her when she is absent.

..................Janet Barr..................
Signature of Pupil

..........Mollie E. Harrington..........
Signature of Teacher

Parents are requested to write their comments and suggestions below and send this card back to school.

Date December 1942

Scholarship Janet continues to do splended work She is an excellent oral reader, and gains the thought readily. This is evident in her work in social studies, in which she displays a keen interest!

Citizenship

She is courteous and helpful Attentive to work, and active and alert in games on the grounds.

Attendance

Psalm 37: 8-11

Leave anger alone.
Do not show yourself heated up only to do wrong yourself.
The gentle spirits will posses the earth
and find exquisite delight in the abundance of peace.